CURRICULUM

Spelling
PRACTICE BOOK

Macmillan McGraw-Hill

CUR
621
MMH
5
2007
SPB

The *McGraw-Hill* Companies

 **Macmillan
McGraw-Hill**

Published by Macmillan/McGraw-Hill, of McGraw-Hill Education, a division of The McGraw-Hill Companies, Inc.,
Two Penn Plaza, New York, New York 10121.

Copyright © by Macmillan/McGraw-Hill. All rights reserved. No part of this publication may be reproduced or
distributed in any form or by any means, or stored in a database or retrieval system, without the prior written
consent of The McGraw-Hill Companies, Inc., including, but not limited to, network storage or transmission, or
broadcast for distance learning.

Printed in the United States of America

2 3 4 5 6 7 8 9 10 024 09 08 07 06 05

Contents

© Macmillan/McGraw-Hill

Unit 2 • Discoveries

© Macmillan/McGraw-Hill

Unit 3 • Turning Points

© Macmillan/McGraw-Hill

Unit 4 • Experiences

© Macmillan/McGraw-Hill

Unit 5 • Achievements

© Macmillan/McGraw-Hill

Unit 6 • Great Ideas

© Macmillan/McGraw-Hill

Name _____

Fold back the paper along the dotted line. Write the words in the blanks as they are read aloud. When you finish the test, unfold the paper. Use the list at the right to correct any spelling mistakes.

1. _____
2. _____
3. _____
4. _____
5. _____
6. _____
7. _____
8. _____
9. _____
10. _____
11. _____
12. _____
13. _____
14. _____
15. _____
16. _____
17. _____
18. _____
19. _____
20. _____

Review Words

21. _____
22. _____
23. _____

Challenge Words

24. _____
25. _____

1. batch
2. rough
3. stump
4. bunch
5. tough
6. nick
7. shrug
8. tenth
9. stuff
10. laugh
11. guess
12. sense
13. damp
14. prop
15. fling
16. gush
17. dove
18. lead
19. notch
20. scan
21. past
22. dock
23. plum
24. cinch
25. blond

© Macmillan/McGraw-Hill

At Home: Help the student practice the words he or she missed to prepare for the Posttest.

Name_____

Using the Word Study Steps

1. LOOK at the word.

2. SAY the word aloud.

3. STUDY the letters in the word.

4. WRITE the word.

5. CHECK the word.
   Did you spell the word right?
   If not, go back to step 1.

Find and Circle

Where are the spelling words?

d	a	m	p	e	f	g	t	e	n	t	h	w	r	t	a	r	l	t	q	g	u	e	s	s	t	u	p	r	o	p	r
b	r	d	s	t	u	m	p	e	l	a	u	g	h	b	z	x	e	n	i	c	k	a	r	t	s	h	r	u	g	e	t
s	c	a	n	t	o	u	g	h	m	t	s	a	p	b	a	t	c	h	e	y	s	e	n	s	e	g	l	u	w	a
g	f	l	i	n	g	i	g	u	s	h	r	o	u	g	h	h	b	u	n	c	h	c	s	t	u	f	f	d	o	v	e
c	k	o	d	h	w	q	l	e	a	d	v	n	o	t	c	h	c	n	i	h	c	l	o	k	m	l	p	u	e	r

Alphabetical Order

Use the lines below to write the spelling words in alphabetical order.

1. _____   6. _____   11. _____   16. _____

2. _____   7. _____   12. _____   17. _____

3. _____   8. _____   13. _____   18. _____

4. _____   9. _____   14. _____   19. _____

5. _____   10. _____   15. _____   20. _____

© Macmillan/McGraw-Hill

At Home: Review the Word Study Steps above to help the
student spell new words.

Name_____

batch	dove	stuff	tenth	tough
nick	fling	notch	scan	stump
rough	shrug	bunch	guess	laugh
lead	gush	damp	prop	sense

Sort each spelling word by finding the sound and spelling pattern to which it belongs.

Short a spelled *a*

1. _____
2. _____
3. _____

Short a spelled *au*

1. _____

Short e spelled *e*

1. _____
2. _____

Short e spelled *ue*

1. _____

Short e spelled *ea*

1. _____

Short i spelled *i*

1. _____
2. _____

Short o spelled *o*

1. _____
2. _____

Short u spelled *u*

1. _____
2. _____
3. _____
4. _____
5. _____

Short u spelled *o*

1. _____

Short u spelled *ou*

1. _____
2. _____

© Macmillan/McGraw-Hill

Name_____

batch	dove	stuff	tenth	tough
nick	fling	notch	scan	stump
rough	shrug	bunch	guess	laugh
lead	gush	damp	prop	sense

Definitions

Write the spelling word that matches each definition below.

1. throw _____

2. wet _____

3. gather _____

4. pour out _____

5. mark _____

6. hold up _____

7. bird _____

8. small cut _____

9. confuse _____

10. not smooth _____

11. group _____

12. read quickly _____

Finish the Sentences

Write the spelling word that best completes each sentence.

13. It was a _____ word to spell.

14. The _____ question was the hardest of all.

15. His answer did not make _____.

16. She was happy and started to _____.

17. She took a _____ because she did not know the answer.

18. He was unsure and answered the question with a _____.

19. He had too much _____ in his desk.

20. She gave him a _____ pencil for the test.

© Macmillan/McGraw-Hill

Name

Circle the misspelled words in the set of instructions. Write the words correctly on the lines below.

You will receive a list of ten words for the spelling bee. Before the contest begins, skain the list of words. The tinth word on the list is a bonus word. Its spelling is unusual and may stumpe you. You will get an extra point if you spell the bonus word correctly.

Here are some tips for the contest. If a word does not make cents to you, ask to hear it again. If you are not sure how to spell a word, take a gess. Last but not least, don't worry if your hands feel dap. That just means you are feeling a little nervous.

1. _____   3. _____   5. _____

2. _____   4. _____   6. _____

Writing Activity

Have you ever watched or taken part in a contest? Write a description of what happened or what you think might happen at a contest, using four spelling words.

_____

_____

_____

_____

_____

_____

_____

_____

_____

_____

© Macmillan/McGraw-Hill

Name_____

Look at the words in each set below. One word in each set is
spelled correctly. Use a pencil to fill in the circle next to the correct
word. Before you begin, look at the sample set of words. Sample
A has been done for you. Do Sample B by yourself. When you are
sure you know what to do, you may go on with the rest of the page.

Sample A:
- Ⓐ lump
- Ⓑ lumpe
- Ⓒ lumpp
- Ⓓ luump

Sample B:
- Ⓔ tacke
- Ⓕ taak
- Ⓖ tack
- Ⓗ takk

1. Ⓐ batch
   Ⓑ bach
   Ⓒ baatch
   Ⓓ bache

2. Ⓔ rugh
   Ⓕ rughe
   Ⓖ rough
   Ⓗ rogh

3. Ⓐ stumpe
   Ⓑ stuump
   Ⓒ stummp
   Ⓓ stump

4. Ⓔ bounch
   Ⓕ bunch
   Ⓖ bunck
   Ⓗ buunch

5. Ⓐ tough
   Ⓑ touff
   Ⓒ tuf
   Ⓓ tugh

6. Ⓔ nik
   Ⓕ nikke
   Ⓖ nicke
   Ⓗ nick

7. Ⓐ shrugg
   Ⓑ shrug
   Ⓒ shruge
   Ⓓ shruug

8. Ⓔ tenth
   Ⓕ teenth
   Ⓖ tenthe
   Ⓗ teenthe

9. Ⓐ stouff
   Ⓑ stuff
   Ⓒ stufe
   Ⓓ stuffe

10. Ⓔ lafe
    Ⓕ laagh
    Ⓖ lagh
    Ⓗ laugh

11. Ⓐ gess
    Ⓑ gues
    Ⓒ guess
    Ⓓ guss

12. Ⓔ sense
    Ⓕ senss
    Ⓖ sens
    Ⓗ seens

13. Ⓐ dampe
    Ⓑ dammp
    Ⓒ daamp
    Ⓓ damp

14. Ⓔ porp
    Ⓕ proop
    Ⓖ prop
    Ⓗ propp

15. Ⓐ fling
    Ⓑ flinge
    Ⓒ fliing
    Ⓓ faling

16. Ⓔ guush
    Ⓕ gushe
    Ⓖ gush
    Ⓗ gussh

17. Ⓐ dove
    Ⓑ duv
    Ⓒ duve
    Ⓓ dov

18. Ⓔ lead
    Ⓕ lede
    Ⓖ leade
    Ⓗ ledd

19. Ⓐ nootch
    Ⓑ noch
    Ⓒ notch
    Ⓓ noutch

20. Ⓔ scane
    Ⓕ scan
    Ⓖ scaan
    Ⓗ scahn

© Macmillan/McGraw-Hill

Name _____

Fold back the paper along the dotted line. Write the words in the blanks as they are read aloud. When you finish the test, unfold the paper. Use the list at the right to correct any spelling mistakes.

1. _____
2. _____
3. _____
4. _____
5. _____
6. _____
7. _____
8. _____
9. _____
10. _____
11. _____
12. _____
13. _____
14. _____
15. _____
16. _____
17. _____
18. _____
19. _____
20. _____

Review Words

21. _____
22. _____
23. _____

Challenge Words

24. _____
25. _____

1. paste
2. bride
3. shave
4. spice
5. greed
6. plead
7. greet
8. heap
9. paid
10. coach
11. theme
12. type
13. oak
14. fame
15. yolk
16. folks
17. aim
18. prey
19. tow
20. grind
21. tenth
22. damp
23. stuff
24. decay
25. lifetime

© Macmillan/McGraw-Hill

At Home: Help the student practice the words he or she missed to prepare for the Posttest.

Name_____

Using the Word Study Steps

1. LOOK at the word.

2. SAY the word aloud.

3. STUDY the letters in the word.

4. WRITE the word.

5. CHECK the word.
   Did you spell the word right?
   If not, go back to step 1.

Find Rhyming Words

Circle the word in each row that rhymes with the word in dark type.

1.	**bride**	raid	tide	rude
2.	**greet**	met	grunt	seat
3.	**shave**	wave	dove	shy
4.	**tow**	toe	too	saw
5.	**prey**	say	eye	pry
6.	**plead**	play	need	head
7.	**heap**	yap	heel	deep
8.	**oak**	joke	oat	neck
9.	**spice**	icy	nice	speck
10.	**type**	ripe	cup	twine
11.	**theme**	then	dream	some
12.	**paid**	pail	mad	parade
13.	**paste**	taste	pass	coast
14.	**aim**	lame	aid	may
15.	**greed**	great	weed	grand

© Macmillan/McGraw-Hill

At Home: Review the Word Study Steps above to help the student spell new words.

Name_____

folks	aim	prey	yolk	greed
greet	grind	fame	heap	coach
oak	paid	paste	plead	shave
theme	bride	tow	spice	type

Sort each spelling word by finding the sound and spelling pattern to which it belongs.

Write the words that have long _a_ spelled:

_ai_	_a-e_	_ey_
1. _____	1. _____	1. _____
2. _____	2. _____	
	3. _____	

Write the words that have long _e_ spelled:

_ee_	_ea_	_e-e_
1. _____	1. _____	1. _____
2. _____	2. _____	

Write the words that have long _i_ spelled:

_i_	_y_	_i-e_
1. _____	1. _____	1. _____
		2. _____

Write the words that have long _o_ spelled:

_o_	_oa_	_ow_
1. _____	1. _____	1. _____
2. _____	2. _____	

© Macmillan/McGraw-Hill

Name_____

folks	aim	prey	yolk	greed
greet	grind	fame	heap	coach
oak	paid	paste	plead	shave
theme	bride	tow	spice	type

Replacements

Write the spelling word that can replace the underlined word or words in each sentence below.

1. Davy wasn't like any <u>kind</u> of person she had ever met. _____

2. He pulled up the trees and threw them in a <u>pile</u>. _____

3. Davy's <u>new wife</u> was as strong as he was. _____

4. He used to <u>say hello to</u> people with a wave of his coonskin cap.

   _____

5. His <u>goal</u> was to pull the tail off Halley's Comet. _____

6. Davy did not want to be <u>given money</u> for anything he did. _____

7. The <u>message</u> of the story is that there is a way to solve every

   problem. _____

8. <u>People</u> everywhere had heard about Davy Crockett. _____

Definitions

Write the spelling word that matches each definition below.

9. part of an egg _____

10. glue _____

11. pull _____

12. beg _____

13. kind of tree _____

14. crush _____

15. hunted animal _____

16. desire for a lot of something

   _____

17. being well known

   _____

18. cut off hair _____

19. wagon pulled by horses

   _____

20. something added to food

   _____

© Macmillan/McGraw-Hill

Name_____

Circle the misspelled words in the passage. Write the words correctly on the lines below.

America is in a hep of trouble. Halley's Comet has made our country its pray. The comet is speeding toward the earth. It is getting bigger every day. If it crashes into the planet, it will grynde everything into small pieces.

Only a special tip of man can stop the comet. That man is Davy Crockett. He lives far away in the mountains. We don't have to pled with him for help. As soon as news of the comet reaches him, he will be on his way. Pulling the tail off the comet won't be a problem for Davy Crockett. He won't even want to be pade for saving the world!

1. _____   3. _____   5. _____

2. _____   4. _____   6. _____

Writing Activity

Suppose that you were bigger than life, like Davy Crockett. What do you imagine you could do? Write a tall tale about yourself, using four spelling words.

_____

_____

_____

_____

_____

_____

_____

_____

_____

© Macmillan/McGraw-Hill

Look at the words in each set below. One word in each set is spelled correctly. Use a pencil to fill in the circle next to the correct word. Before you begin, look at the sample set of words. Sample A has been done for you. Do Sample B by yourself. When you are sure you know what to do, you may go on with the rest of the page.

Sample A:
- Ⓐ doom
- Ⓑ dume
- Ⓒ duum
- Ⓓ doome

Sample B:
- Ⓔ taik
- Ⓕ taak
- Ⓖ take
- Ⓗ tehk

1. Ⓐ fokes
   Ⓑ folks
   Ⓒ fokse
   Ⓓ fohks

2. Ⓔ ame
   Ⓕ aame
   Ⓖ aime
   Ⓗ aim

3. Ⓐ prey
   Ⓑ preye
   Ⓒ praiy
   Ⓓ prai

4. Ⓔ yok
   Ⓕ yolke
   Ⓖ yolk
   Ⓗ yohk

5. Ⓐ greed
   Ⓑ grede
   Ⓒ greid
   Ⓓ gried

6. Ⓔ grete
   Ⓕ greet
   Ⓖ greit
   Ⓗ griet

7. Ⓐ grinde
   Ⓑ grind
   Ⓒ gihnd
   Ⓓ griind

8. Ⓔ fame
   Ⓕ faym
   Ⓖ fam
   Ⓗ faime

9. Ⓐ heep
   Ⓑ hepe
   Ⓒ heap
   Ⓓ heape

10. Ⓔ coche
    Ⓕ coach
    Ⓖ coch
    Ⓗ coache

11. Ⓐ ohk
    Ⓑ oke
    Ⓒ oak
    Ⓓ ock

12. Ⓔ paid
    Ⓕ pade
    Ⓖ payed
    Ⓗ paad

13. Ⓐ paste
    Ⓑ paist
    Ⓒ paast
    Ⓓ paiste

14. Ⓔ pleed
    Ⓕ plede
    Ⓖ pleid
    Ⓗ plead

15. Ⓐ shaiv
    Ⓑ shave
    Ⓒ shav
    Ⓓ shaive

16. Ⓔ heem
    Ⓕ theim
    Ⓖ theeme
    Ⓗ theme

17. Ⓐ brid
    Ⓑ bride
    Ⓒ briid
    Ⓓ briide

18. Ⓔ toh
    Ⓕ towe
    Ⓖ tow
    Ⓗ tohe

19. Ⓐ spyce
    Ⓑ spihc
    Ⓒ spihce
    Ⓓ spice

20. Ⓔ tipe
    Ⓕ type
    Ⓖ tighp
    Ⓗ typ

© Macmillan/McGraw-Hill

Name_____

Fold back the paper along the dotted line. Write the words in the blanks as they are read aloud. When you finish the test, unfold the paper. Use the list at the right to correct any spelling mistakes.

1. _____
2. _____
3. _____
4. _____
5. _____
6. _____
7. _____
8. _____
9. _____
10. _____
11. _____
12. _____
13. _____
14. _____
15. _____
16. _____
17. _____
18. _____
19. _____
20. _____

Review Words 21. _____
22. _____
23. _____

Challenge Words 24. _____
25. _____

1. tuna
2. duty
3. lose
4. few
5. doom
6. bamboo
7. brood
8. crooks
9. hoof
10. hooks
11. booth
12. handbook
13. prove
14. mute
15. amuse
16. plume
17. hue
18. view
19. bruise
20. union
21. theme
22. coach
23. bride
24. strewn
25. accuse

© Macmillan/McGraw-Hill

At Home: Help the student practice the words he or she missed to prepare for the Posttest.

Name_____

Using the Word Study Steps

1. LOOK at the word.

2. SAY the word aloud.

3. STUDY the letters in the word.

4. WRITE the word.

5. CHECK the word.
   Did you spell the word right?
   If not, go back to step 1.

Find Rhyming Words

Circle the word in each row that rhymes with the word in dark type.

1. **lose**	choose	close	lost
2. **booth**	both	tooth	comb
3. **hue**	who	would	cue
4. **mute**	cute	mood	flunk
5. **duty**	sooty	fruity	dust
6. **view**	grow	shoes	few
7. **plume**	gloom	plunk	put
8. **crooks**	rocks	rooks	cools
9. **brood**	mood	broke	brook
10. **bruise**	brush	burn	cruise
11. **prove**	shove	move	dove
12. **doom**	room	dorm	dome
13. **hoof**	roof	half	woof
14. **few**	feud	stew	fool
15. **amuse**	confuse	amidst	among

At Home: Review the Word Study Steps above to help the student spell new words.

© Macmillan/McGraw-Hill

Name

amuse   bamboo   brood   crooks   tuna
doom   few   view   hoof   hooks
hue   bruise   booth   lose   duty
handbook   prove   mute   plume   union

Sort each spelling word by finding the sound and spelling pattern to which it belongs.

Write the words that have /ü/ spelled:

u

1. _____
2. _____

o-e

1. _____
2. _____

u-e

1. _____

oo

1. _____
2. _____
3. _____
4. _____

ui

1. _____

Write the words that have /ū/ spelled:

u-e

1. _____
2. _____
3. _____

u

1. _____

ew

1. _____
2. _____

Write the words that have /ů/ spelled:

oo

1. _____
2. _____
3. _____
4. _____

© Macmillan/McGraw-Hill

Name_____

amuse	bamboo	brood	crooks	tuna
doom	few	view	hoof	hooks
hue	bruise	booth	lose	duty
handbook	prove	mute	plume	union

Fill in the Blank

Write the spelling word that best completes each sentence.

1. Banana trees, rubber trees, and _____ grow in tropical rain forests.

2. The canopy of trees in a rain forest blocks the _____ of the sky.

3. A _____ of smoke rose over the forest.

4. _____ plants can grow in the soil of coniferous forests.

5. Deciduous trees _____ their leaves in the fall.

6. It is everyone's _____ to protect forests.

7. The leaves have a beautiful _____ in autumn.

8. He found its name in a _____ to trees in North America.

Similar Meanings

Write the spelling word that has the same, or almost the same, meaning.

9. silent _____

10. bump _____

11. worry _____

12. animal foot _____

13. entertain _____

14. bent pieces of metal _____

15. box-like space _____

16. coming together _____

17. show _____

18. large fish _____

19. disaster _____

20. dishonest people _____

© Macmillan/McGraw-Hill

Name_____

Circle the misspelled words in the paragraph. Write the words correctly on the lines below.

    Our backyard has only a fue trees. The big maple tree is my favorite. I have a good vyoo of it from my room. All the trees in the yard are deciduous. They all loos their leaves in the fall. Before that happens, though, their leaves change color. The maple's leaves turn a red hiew. I amewz myself by collecting maple leaves each fall. Once I found a ploom from a bird on the ground by the maple. I saved it along with the leaves I had collected.

1. _____   3. _____   5. _____

2. _____   4. _____   6. _____

Writing Activity

Write about something in nature that interests you. Use four spelling words in your description.

_____

_____

_____

_____

_____

_____

_____

_____

_____

_____

_____

© Macmillan/McGraw-Hill

Name_____

Look at the words in each set below. One word in each set is spelled correctly. Use a pencil to fill in the circle next to the correct word. Before you begin, look at the sample set of words. Sample A has been done for you. Do Sample B by yourself. When you are sure you know what to do, you may go on with the rest of the page.

Sample A:
- Ⓐ loot
- Ⓑ lut
- Ⓒ loote
- Ⓓ lote

Sample B:
- Ⓔ tock
- Ⓕ tuk
- Ⓖ took
- Ⓗ tuke

1. Ⓐ amuse Ⓑ amyuse Ⓒ amyoos Ⓓ amoose
2. Ⓔ bambu Ⓕ bamboo Ⓖ bambuu Ⓗ bambo
3. Ⓐ broode Ⓑ brood Ⓒ brode Ⓓ brod
4. Ⓔ croks Ⓕ crokes Ⓖ crooks Ⓗ crookes
5. Ⓐ toona Ⓑ tuna Ⓒ tuuna Ⓓ tona

6. Ⓔ dume Ⓕ doom Ⓖ dum Ⓗ doome
7. Ⓐ fyoo Ⓑ few Ⓒ foo Ⓓ fu
8. Ⓔ vu Ⓕ vyoo Ⓖ view Ⓗ voo
9. Ⓐ huf Ⓑ hof Ⓒ hoof Ⓓ huuf
10. Ⓔ hucks Ⓕ hookes Ⓖ hukes Ⓗ hooks

11. Ⓐ hue Ⓑ hoo Ⓒ hyoo Ⓓ hu
12. Ⓔ bruise Ⓕ broose Ⓖ broos Ⓗ bruse
13. Ⓐ buthe Ⓑ boothe Ⓒ booth Ⓓ buth
14. Ⓔ lose Ⓕ loos Ⓖ luse Ⓗ lus
15. Ⓐ dootee Ⓑ duty Ⓒ dooty Ⓓ dutey

16. Ⓔ handbook Ⓕ handbuk Ⓖ handbooke Ⓗ handbuke
17. Ⓐ proove Ⓑ proov Ⓒ prove Ⓓ pruve
18. Ⓔ myoot Ⓕ moote Ⓖ mute Ⓗ miut
19. Ⓐ ploom Ⓑ plume Ⓒ ploome Ⓓ pluhm
20. Ⓔ oonon Ⓕ unon Ⓖ unun Ⓗ union

© Macmillan/McGraw-Hill

Name_____

Fold back the paper along the dotted line. Write the words in the blanks as they are read aloud. When you finish the test, unfold the paper. Use the list at the right to correct any spelling mistakes.

1. _____
2. _____
3. _____
4. _____
5. _____
6. _____
7. _____
8. _____
9. _____
10. _____
11. _____
12. _____
13. _____
14. _____
15. _____
16. _____
17. _____
18. _____
19. _____
20. _____

Review Words 21. _____

22. _____

23. _____

Challenge Words 24. _____

25. _____

1. heart
2. swear
3. aboard
4. squares
5. swore
6. chart
7. scorn
8. starch
9. source
10. fare
11. barge
12. thorn
13. marsh
14. force
15. harsh
16. scarce
17. coarse
18. flare
19. course
20. sword
21. brood
22. prove
23. hoof
24. uproar
25. gorge

At Home: Help the student practice the words he or she missed to prepare for the Posttest.

© Macmillan/McGraw-Hill

Name_____

Using the Word Study Steps

1. LOOK at the word.

2. SAY the word aloud.

3. STUDY the letters in the word.

4. WRITE the word.

5. CHECK the word.
   Did you spell the word right?
   If not, go back to step 1.

Fill-Ins

Fill in the missing letters of each word to form a spelling word.

1. m ____ ____ sh

2. h ____ ____ ____ t

3. f ____ ____ e

4. st ____ ____ ch

5. th ____ ____ n

6. ab ____ ____ ____ d

7. squ ____ ____ es

8. sw ____ ____ e

9. f ____ ____ ce

10. sw ____ ____ r

11. c ____ ____ ____ se

12. sw ____ ____ d

13. b ____ ____ ge

14. h ____ ____ sh

15. sc ____ ____ n

16. sc ____ ____ ce

17. fl ____ ____ e

18. s ____ ____ ____ ce

19. c ____ ____ ____ se

20. ch ____ ____ t

Use the words above to help you write a poem of at least 4 lines.

21. _____

22. _____

23. _____

24. _____

© Macmillan/McGraw-Hill

At Home: Review the Word Study Steps above to help the
student spell new words.

Name_____

force	scorn	sword	swore	source
aboard	course	coarse	chart	barge
harsh	marsh	starch	heart	scarce
squares	swear	flare	fare	thorn

Sort each spelling word by finding the sound and spelling pattern to which it belongs.

Write the words that have /är/ spelled:

ar

1. _____   4. _____

2. _____   5. _____

3. _____

ear

1. _____

Write the words that have /âr/ spelled:

ar   *are*

1. _____   1. _____

2. _____

3. _____   *ear*

1. _____

Write the words that have /ôr/ spelled:

our   *ore*

1. _____   1. _____

2. _____

or   *oar*

1. _____   1. _____

2. _____   2. _____

3. _____

4. _____

© Macmillan/McGraw-Hill

Name_____

force	scorn	sword	swore	source
aboard	course	coarse	chart	barge
harsh	marsh	starch	heart	scarce
squares	swear	flare	fare	thorn

Fill in the Blanks

Write the spelling word that best completes each sentence.

1. Only the astronauts were allowed _____ the spacecraft.

2. Her _____ beat quickly as she listened to the countdown.

3. Scientists tracked the _____ of the spacecraft.

4. The _____ of gravity is weaker on the Moon than on Earth.

5. The astronauts' jobs for each day were listed on a _____.

6. The _____ of the rockets could be seen for miles.

7. Their landing was _____, but nothing was damaged.

8. He _____ that he would return to the Moon one day.

Related Words

Write the spelling word that is related to the sets of words below.

9. circles, triangles, _____

10. rough, stiff _____

11. swamp, bog, _____

12. needle, spike, _____

13. soap, water, _____

14. promise, pledge, _____

15. blade, weapon, _____

16. boat, ship, _____

17. price, charge, _____

18. rare, limited, _____

19. hatred, dislike, _____

20. beginning, cause, _____

© Macmillan/McGraw-Hill

Name_____

Circle the misspelled words in the message. Write the words correctly on the lines below.

Dear Tyra,

We have been abored the spacecraft for two days now. Everything is going smoothly. We are right on corce to reach the space station. You can see where we are if you look at the cheart I gave you.

It's hard to describe what it felt like to blast off from Earth. The fours of the rockets was incredible. We couldn't see the flare of the rockets when we took off. I bet you had a good view, though. I sware my hart skipped a beat. I wonder how you felt as you watched the spacecraft lift off.

I'll be home sooner than you think. Take care of your little brother!

Love, Dad

1. _____   3. _____   5. _____

2. _____   4. _____   6. _____

Writing Activity

Imagine that you are on a space trip. Write an e-mail message home to a friend or your family. Use four spelling words in your message.

_____

_____

_____

_____

_____

_____

_____

© Macmillan/McGraw-Hill

Name_____

Look at the words in each set below. One word in each set is
spelled correctly. Use a pencil to fill in the circle next to the correct
word. Before you begin, look at the sample set of words. Sample
A has been done for you. Do Sample B by yourself. When you are
sure you know what to do, you may go on with the rest of the page.

Sample A:

Ⓐ spot
Ⓑ spott
Ⓒ spote
Ⓓ spoht

Sample B:

Ⓔ taak
Ⓕ taik
Ⓖ take
Ⓗ tak

1. Ⓐ force
   Ⓑ fohrce
   Ⓒ fors
   Ⓓ fource

2. Ⓔ skohrn
   Ⓕ scorne
   Ⓖ scorn
   Ⓗ skorn

3. Ⓐ sorde
   Ⓑ sword
   Ⓒ sord
   Ⓓ soord

4. Ⓔ swor
   Ⓕ sooor
   Ⓖ suore
   Ⓗ swore

5. Ⓐ sorce
   Ⓑ source
   Ⓒ sors
   Ⓓ sohrce

6. Ⓔ aboard
   Ⓕ abourd
   Ⓖ aborde
   Ⓗ abord

7. Ⓐ corse
   Ⓑ cohrs
   Ⓒ coarse
   Ⓓ coors

8. Ⓔ corse
   Ⓕ cohrs
   Ⓖ course
   Ⓗ coors

9. Ⓐ chort
   Ⓑ charte
   Ⓒ chart
   Ⓓ chorte

10. Ⓔ borje
    Ⓕ barg
    Ⓖ barge
    Ⓗ bahrge

11. Ⓐ horsh
    Ⓑ harshe
    Ⓒ haarsh
    Ⓓ harsh

12. Ⓔ marsh
    Ⓕ maarsh
    Ⓖ morsh
    Ⓗ marshe

13. Ⓐ staarch
    Ⓑ starche
    Ⓒ starch
    Ⓓ storch

14. Ⓔ haart
    Ⓕ hahrt
    Ⓖ heart
    Ⓗ harte

15. Ⓐ scarce
    Ⓑ scaerce
    Ⓒ scearce
    Ⓓ scarc

16. Ⓔ skwaers
    Ⓕ squares
    Ⓖ squeres
    Ⓗ squarez

17. Ⓐ sware
    Ⓑ swar
    Ⓒ swear
    Ⓓ swere

18. Ⓔ flaere
    Ⓕ flar
    Ⓖ flare
    Ⓗ flaer

19. Ⓐ faer
    Ⓑ faar
    Ⓒ fare
    Ⓓ fer

20. Ⓔ thorne
    Ⓕ thorn
    Ⓖ thohrn
    Ⓗ thourn

© Macmillan/McGraw-Hill

Name_____

Fold back the paper along the dotted line. Write the words in the blanks as they are read aloud. When you finish the test, unfold the paper. Use the list at the right to correct any spelling mistakes.

1. _____   1. year
2. _____   2. nerve
3. _____   3. surf
4. _____   4. verse
5. _____   5. clear
6. _____   6. squirm
7. _____   7. dreary
8. _____   8. jeer
9. _____   9. thirst
10. _____   10. sneer
11. _____   11. squirt
12. _____   12. lurk
13. _____   13. yearns
14. _____   14. spurts
15. _____   15. swerve
16. _____   16. stern
17. _____   17. blurt
18. _____   18. lurch
19. _____   19. spur
20. _____   20. engineer

Review Words 21. _____   21. aboard
22. _____   22. barge
23. _____   23. scarce

Challenge Words 24. _____   24. smear
25. _____   25. rehearse

© Macmillan/McGraw-Hill

At Home: Help the student practice the words he or she missed to prepare for the Posttest.

Pipiolo and the Roof Dogs **25**
Grade 5/Unit 1

Name_____

Using the Word Study Steps

1. LOOK at the word.

2. SAY the word aloud.

3. STUDY the letters in the word.

4. WRITE the word.

5. CHECK the word.
Did you spell the word right?
If not, go back to step 1.

Where Are the Spelling Words?

Find and circle the spelling words in this puzzle.

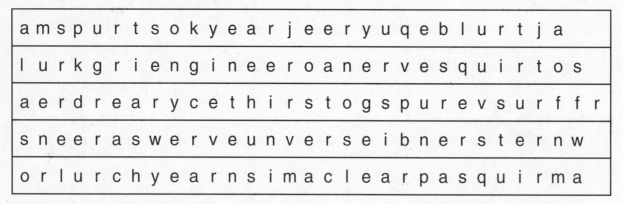

```
a m s p u r t s o k y e a r j e e r y u q e b l u r t j a
l u r k g r i e n g i n e e r o a n e r v e s q u i r t o s
a e r d r e a r y c e t h i r s t o g s p u r e v s u r f f r
s n e e r a s w e r v e u n v e r s e i b n e r s t e r n w
o r l u r c h y e a r n s i m a c l e a r p a s q u i r m a
```

Make a Puzzle

Make up a puzzle of your own using the space on this page. Give it to someone else to solve. Be sure to include at least five spelling words in your puzzle.

© Macmillan/McGraw-Hill

At Home: Review the Word Study Steps above to help the student spell new words.

Name _____

squirm	dreary	nerve	squirt	verse
surf	lurk	swerve	stern	spurts
lurch	blurt	thirst	spur	engineer
jeer	sneer	clear	year	yearns

Sort each spelling word by finding the sound and spelling pattern to which it belongs.

Write the words that have /ûr/ spelled:

er

1. _____
2. _____
3. _____
4. _____

ir

1. _____
2. _____
3. _____

ur

1. _____
2. _____
3. _____
4. _____
5. _____
6. _____

ear

1. _____

Write the words that have /îr/ spelled:

ear

1. _____
2. _____
3. _____

eer

1. _____
2. _____
3. _____

© Macmillan/McGraw-Hill

Name_____

squirm	dreary	nerve	squirt	verse
surf	lurk	swerve	stern	spurts
lurch	blurt	thirst	spur	engineer
jeer	sneer	clear	year	yearns

Opposites

Write the spelling word whose meaning is the opposite of each clue below.

1. smiling _____

2. applaud _____

3. cheery _____

4. be still _____

5. cloudy _____

6. smile warmly _____

Fill in the Blank

Write the spelling word that best completes each sentence.

7. Every roof dog _____ to be free.

8. Most dogs do not have the _____ to escape.

9. They _____ in the shadows of the buildings.

10. A _____ is too long to be tied up.

11. The dogs would _____ at anyone who passed by.

12. They would bark in _____ during the day.

13. Pipiolo would _____ out a bark in reply.

14. He would _____ away from the other dogs.

15. He tried to _____ them to escape.

16. It would take an _____ to break their chains.

17. Lupe wanted to take Pipiolo for a run in the _____.

18. She liked to _____ water in his mouth.

19. He had a great _____ for water.

20. Lupe sang a _____ of her favorite song to him.

© Macmillan/McGraw-Hill

Name _____

Circle the misspelled words in the diary entry below. Write the words correctly on the lines below.

Dear Diary,

    The roof dogs will never jere at Pipiolo again. Today he was the enginear of their escape. Pipiolo knew the dogs finally had the nurv to break free. He gave them cler instructions about what to do. Then he told the dogs to wait. A little later, a truck came up the road to the village to deliver oranges. The dogs jumped into the back of the truck. With a lirch, the truck headed out of the village. The roof dogs had left their drery lives behind!

1. _____ 3. _____ 5. _____

2. _____ 4. _____ 6. _____

Writing Activity

Pretend that Pipiolo is your pet dog. Write a paragraph about what you and Pipiolo might do together. Use four words from the spelling list.

_____

_____

_____

_____

_____

_____

_____

_____

_____

© Macmillan/McGraw-Hill

Name_____

Look at the words in each set below. One word in each set is spelled correctly. Use a pencil to fill in the circle next to the correct word. Before you begin, look at the sample set of words. Sample A has been done for you. Do Sample B by yourself. When you are sure you know what to do, you may go on with the rest of the page.

Sample A:

Ⓐ first
Ⓑ furst
Ⓒ foorst
Ⓓ fuhrst

Sample B:

Ⓔ deir
Ⓕ dere
Ⓖ deer
Ⓗ der

1. Ⓐ skwirm
   Ⓑ squirm
   Ⓒ sqirm
   Ⓓ sqoorm

2. Ⓔ dreery
   Ⓕ drery
   Ⓖ dreary
   Ⓗ drerey

3. Ⓐ nerve
   Ⓑ nurv
   Ⓒ nirv
   Ⓓ nirve

4. Ⓔ skwirt
   Ⓕ sqirt
   Ⓖ sqoort
   Ⓗ squirt

5. Ⓐ verss
   Ⓑ virse
   Ⓒ verse
   Ⓓ virs

6. Ⓔ surf
   Ⓕ sirf
   Ⓖ soorf
   Ⓗ surfe

7. Ⓐ lurk
   Ⓑ loork
   Ⓒ lurke
   Ⓓ lerke

8. Ⓔ swurve
   Ⓕ swurv
   Ⓖ swerve
   Ⓗ swirve

9. Ⓐ stirn
   Ⓑ sturne
   Ⓒ sturn
   Ⓓ stern

10. Ⓔ spurtes
    Ⓕ sperts
    Ⓖ spurts
    Ⓗ spourts

11. Ⓐ lirtch
    Ⓑ lirch
    Ⓒ lurche
    Ⓓ lurch

12. Ⓔ blurt
    Ⓕ blirt
    Ⓖ blerte
    Ⓗ blert

13. Ⓐ thurst
    Ⓑ therst
    Ⓒ thirst
    Ⓓ thirste

14. Ⓔ spir
    Ⓕ spurre
    Ⓖ spur
    Ⓗ spuhr

15. Ⓐ engineer
    Ⓑ enginire
    Ⓒ enginir
    Ⓓ enginere

16. Ⓔ jeir
    Ⓕ jere
    Ⓖ jeer
    Ⓗ jir

17. Ⓐ snir
    Ⓑ sneer
    Ⓒ snere
    Ⓓ snear

18. Ⓔ clir
    Ⓕ cleer
    Ⓖ clere
    Ⓗ clear

19. Ⓐ yir
    Ⓑ yeer
    Ⓒ yere
    Ⓓ year

20. Ⓔ yurns
    Ⓕ yearns
    Ⓖ yirns
    Ⓗ yerns

© Macmillan/McGraw-Hill

Read each sentence. If an underlined word is spelled wrong, fill in the circle that goes with that word. If no word is spelled wrong, fill in the circle below NONE. Read Sample A and do Sample B.

A. He <u>paid</u> for the last <u>batch</u> of <u>bambu</u>.
   A   B   C

A. Ⓐ Ⓑ ⓒ Ⓓ NONE

B. The <u>engineer</u> climbed <u>aboard</u> the <u>barge</u>.
   E   F   G

B. Ⓔ Ⓕ Ⓖ Ⓗ NONE

1. He made a <u>notch</u> in the <u>aok</u> tree with his <u>sword</u>.
   A   B   C

1. Ⓐ Ⓑ ⓒ Ⓓ NONE

2. She had the <u>nerve</u> to <u>bloort</u> out a <u>harsh</u> word.
   E   F   G

2. Ⓔ Ⓕ Ⓖ Ⓗ NONE

3. The <u>marsh</u> was <u>damp</u> and <u>dreery</u>.
   A   B   C

3. Ⓐ Ⓑ ⓒ Ⓓ NONE

4. It was his <u>dooty</u> to <u>prove</u> that he knew the <u>handbook</u> well.
   E   F   G

4. Ⓔ Ⓕ Ⓖ Ⓗ NONE

5. The <u>coach</u> knew that <u>foo</u> players could run the <u>course</u>.
   A   B   C

5. Ⓐ Ⓑ ⓒ Ⓓ NONE

6. We had the good <u>sense</u> to <u>laff</u> at his <u>guess</u>.
   E   F   G

6. Ⓔ Ⓕ Ⓖ Ⓗ NONE

7. The <u>hoof</u> of the <u>prey</u> was clearly in <u>vieu</u>.
   A   B   C

7. Ⓐ Ⓑ ⓒ Ⓓ NONE

8. The <u>bride</u> started to <u>gush</u> when she heard the kind
   E   F

   words of her <u>fokes</u>.
               G

8. Ⓔ Ⓕ Ⓖ Ⓗ NONE

9. The <u>oak</u> branches lay in a <u>heap</u> by the <u>stumpf</u>.
   A   B   C

9. Ⓐ Ⓑ ⓒ Ⓓ NONE

10. The <u>bryde</u> walked over to <u>greet</u> the groom's <u>folks</u>.
    E   F   G

10. Ⓔ Ⓕ Ⓖ Ⓗ NONE

© Macmillan/McGraw-Hill

Name_____

11. He began to <u>brood</u> over the <u>scorn</u> in his <u>haert</u>.
               A   B   C

NONE
11. Ⓐ Ⓑ Ⓒ Ⓓ

12. The <u>enginear</u> found the <u>source</u> of the <u>plume</u> of smoke.
        E   F   G

NONE
12. Ⓔ Ⓕ Ⓖ Ⓗ

13. The <u>crooks</u> <u>swore</u> that they did not have the <u>stough</u>.
        A   B   C

NONE
13. Ⓐ Ⓑ Ⓒ Ⓓ

14. The <u>sord</u> left a <u>nick</u> in the <u>stump</u>.
        E   F   G

NONE
14. Ⓔ Ⓕ Ⓖ Ⓗ

15. He will <u>grind</u> the <u>stump</u> into a <u>heape</u> of sawdust.
        A   B   C

NONE
15. Ⓐ Ⓑ Ⓒ Ⓓ

16. It was her <u>duty</u> to <u>pay</u> the <u>fare</u> on time.
        E   F   G

NONE
16. Ⓔ Ⓕ Ⓖ Ⓗ

17. She tried to <u>swerve</u> and <u>lurch</u> to avoid the phone <u>bewth</u>.
          A   B   C

NONE
17. Ⓐ Ⓑ Ⓒ Ⓓ

18. The <u>engineer</u> read each <u>vurse</u> from the <u>handbook</u>.
      E   F   G

NONE
18. Ⓔ Ⓕ Ⓖ Ⓗ

19. He noticed that a <u>few</u> <u>hoof</u> prints led into the <u>surhf</u>.
            A   B   C

NONE
19. Ⓐ Ⓑ Ⓒ Ⓓ

20. I can <u>guess</u> from your <u>laugh</u> that the <u>stuff</u> is gone.
      E   F   G

NONE
20. Ⓔ Ⓕ Ⓖ Ⓗ

21. The <u>barge</u> will <u>tow</u> the catch of <u>twona</u>.
        A   B   C

NONE
21. Ⓐ Ⓑ Ⓒ Ⓓ

22. In her <u>view</u>, he remained <u>meyoot</u> in the face of <u>scorn</u>.
        E   F   G

NONE
22. Ⓔ Ⓕ Ⓖ Ⓗ

23. The crowd started to <u>jeer</u> at the <u>crucks</u> for their <u>greed</u>.
            A   B   C

NONE
23. Ⓐ Ⓑ Ⓒ Ⓓ

24. She <u>yurns</u> to <u>lurk</u> by the <u>oak</u> tree.
        E   F   G

NONE
24. Ⓔ Ⓕ Ⓖ Ⓗ

25. His <u>folks</u> thought that the <u>tuna</u> tasted <u>tuff</u>.
      A   B   C

NONE
25. Ⓐ Ⓑ Ⓒ Ⓓ

© Macmillan/McGraw-Hill

Name _____

Fold back the paper along the dotted line. Write the words in the blanks as they are read aloud. When you finish the test, unfold the paper. Use the list at the right to correct any spelling mistakes.

1. _____
2. _____
3. _____
4. _____
5. _____
6. _____
7. _____
8. _____
9. _____
10. _____
11. _____
12. _____
13. _____
14. _____
15. _____
16. _____
17. _____
18. _____
19. _____
20. _____

Review Words 21. _____
22. _____
23. _____

Challenge Words 24. _____
25. _____

1. afternoon
2. background
3. overcome
4. pillowcase
5. rooftop
6. flagpole
7. footstep
8. vice president
9. cornfield
10. cornmeal
11. ice-skating
12. cardboard
13. field trip
14. ninety-one
15. eggshell
16. all right
17. cheerleader
18. armchair
19. earthworm
20. mountaintop
21. blurt
22. jeer
23. thirst
24. first-class
25. briefcase

© Macmillan/McGraw-Hill

At Home: Help the student practice the words he or she missed to prepare for the Posttest.

Shiloh • Grade 5/Unit 2   **33**

Name_____

Using the Word Study Steps

1. LOOK at the word.

2. SAY the word aloud.

3. STUDY the letters in the word.

4. WRITE the word.

5. CHECK the word.
Did you spell the word right?
If not, go back to step 1.

Bits and Pieces

Join the first word on the left with the second word on the right that completes each compound spelling word. Match words 1–10 first, then match words 11–20.

1. mountain	_____	field	**11.** pillow	_____	step
2. cheer	_____	ground	**12.** after	_____	trip
3. back	_____	worm	**13.** vice	_____	case
4. ice-	_____	right	**14.** foot	_____	meal
5. over	_____	shell	**15.** roof	_____	chair
6. corn	_____	top	**16.** arm	_____	top
7. all	_____	skating	**17.** flag	_____	noon
8. egg	_____	board	**18.** field	_____	one
9. earth	_____	come	**19.** corn	_____	president
10. card	_____	leader	**20.** ninety-	_____	pole

© Macmillan/McGraw-Hill

At Home: Review the Word Study Steps above to help the
student spell new words.

Name_____

afternoon	background	cornfield	cornmeal	earthworm
flagpole	footstep	mountaintop	overcome	pillowcase
rooftop	cardboard	ice-skating	ninety-one	vice president
all right	field trip	armchair	cheerleader	eggshell

Open or Closed?

Sort the spelling words according to the pattern by which they form compound words.

One Word

1. _____
2. _____
3. _____
4. _____
5. _____
6. _____
7. _____
8. _____
9. _____
10. _____
11. _____
12. _____
13. _____
14. _____
15. _____

Two Words

1. _____
2. _____
3. _____

Hyphenated

1. _____
2. _____

© Macmillan/McGraw-Hill

Name_____

afternoon   background   cornfield   cornmeal   earthworm
flagpole   footstep   mountaintop overcome   pillowcase
rooftop   cardboard   ice-skating ninety-one   vice president
all right   field trip   armchair   cheerleader eggshell

Meaning Match

Write the spelling word that matches each clue below

1. gliding on ice   _____
2. high part of house   _____
3. to conquer   _____
4. class outing   _____
5. box material   _____
6. middle of day   _____
7. shelter for bird   _____
8. place to sit   _____

9. walking sound   _____
10. no problem   _____
11. a peak   _____
12. crops grow here   _____
13. lives in dirt   _____
14. shouts at sports   _____
15. 30 + 30 + 31   _____

Sentence Derby

Fill in the sentences below with the correct spelling word.

16. Sarah fed _____ to the little bird.

17. Harry was elected _____ of his class.

18. Marty lined the dog's bed with a _____ stuffed with straw.

19. Mary checked the dog's _____ to see if he had an owner.

20. The children designed a banner for the _____.

© Macmillan/McGraw-Hill

Name

Circle the misspelled words in this story. Write the words correctly on the lines below.

Tracy found a kitten outside the iceskating rink. She asked her mother if it would be alrite to take the kitten home. At first, the kitten was fearful. It would shake when it heard a footstep or any loud noise. Tracy took good care of it and helped it overcome its fear. She lined a card-board box with a pillow case for its bed. She sat in the arm chair all afternoon with the cat curled in her lap. Tracy tried to find out the cat's back ground, but no one knew anything about it. Finally, her parents let her keep it!

1. _____   3. _____   5. _____

2. _____   4. _____   6. _____

Writing Activity

Make up a story about a person who is kind to an animal. Write your story in the space below. Use four spelling words.

_____

_____

_____

_____

_____

_____

_____

_____

_____

_____

_____

_____

© Macmillan/McGraw-Hill

Name_____

Look at the words in each set below. One word in each set is spelled correctly. Use a pencil to fill in the circle next to the correct word. Before you begin, look at the sample set of words. Sample A has been done for you. Do Sample B by yourself. When you are sure you know what to do, you may go on with the rest of the page.

Sample A:

Ⓐ chainsaw
Ⓑ chanesaw
Ⓒ chainesaw
Ⓓ chaynesaw

Sample B:

Ⓔ bakyard
Ⓕ backyard
Ⓖ backeyard
Ⓗ bacyardae

1. Ⓐ afternoon
   Ⓑ afternon
   Ⓒ afternune
   Ⓓ aphternoon

6. Ⓔ flaggpole
   Ⓕ flagpol
   Ⓖ flagpoll
   Ⓗ flagpole

11. Ⓐ roofetop
    Ⓑ rooftopp
    Ⓒ rooftop
    Ⓓ rooftoppe

16. Ⓔ awl right
    Ⓕ all rite
    Ⓖ all right
    Ⓗ al rite

2. Ⓔ bacground
   Ⓕ bakground
   Ⓖ background
   Ⓗ backgraund

7. Ⓐ footstepp
   Ⓑ footstep
   Ⓒ footestep
   Ⓓ footsteppe

12. Ⓔ cardboard
    Ⓕ cardeboard
    Ⓖ cardbord
    Ⓗ cardbored

17. Ⓐ field trip
    Ⓑ feeld trip
    Ⓒ field tripp
    Ⓓ field tryp

3. Ⓐ kornfield
   Ⓑ cornfeeld
   Ⓒ cornfeild
   Ⓓ cornfield

8. Ⓔ mountaintop
   Ⓕ mountentop
   Ⓖ mountaintopp
   Ⓗ mountainetop

13. Ⓐ ce-skatting
    Ⓑ eice-skating
    Ⓒ ice-skateng
    Ⓓ ice-skating

18. Ⓔ armchair
    Ⓕ armchare
    Ⓖ armchar
    Ⓗ armchaire

4. Ⓔ cornmeel
   Ⓕ cornmeal
   Ⓖ cornmele
   Ⓗ cornemeal

9. Ⓐ overcomme
   Ⓑ overcome
   Ⓒ overrcome
   Ⓓ overcom

14. Ⓔ ninty-one
    Ⓕ ninedy-one
    Ⓖ ninety-one
    Ⓗ neinty-one

19. Ⓐ chearleader
    Ⓑ cheerleeder
    Ⓒ cheerleader
    Ⓓ chereleader

5. Ⓐ earthworm
   Ⓑ erthworm
   Ⓒ earthwirm
   Ⓓ erthwirm

10. Ⓔ pilowcase
    Ⓕ pilloughcase
    Ⓖ pillocase
    Ⓗ pillowcase

15. Ⓐ vice president
    Ⓑ vise president
    Ⓒ vice pressident
    Ⓓ vic president

20. Ⓔ egshell
    Ⓕ eggshell
    Ⓖ eggshel
    Ⓗ egshel

© Macmillan/McGraw-Hill

Name _____

Fold back the paper along the dotted line. Write the words in the blanks as they are read aloud. When you finish the test, unfold the paper. Use the list at the right to correct any spelling mistakes.

1. _____
2. _____
3. _____
4. _____
5. _____
6. _____
7. _____
8. _____
9. _____
10. _____
11. _____
12. _____
13. _____
14. _____
15. _____
16. _____
17. _____
18. _____
19. _____
20. _____

Review Words 21. _____
22. _____
23. _____

Challenge Words 24. _____
25. _____

1. rattlers
2. fangs
3. countries
4. liberties
5. potatoes
6. rodeos
7. taxes
8. reptiles
9. surroundings
10. beliefs
11. difficulties
12. batches
13. abilities
14. lashes
15. identities
16. losses
17. possibilities
18. notches
19. zeroes
20. eddies
21. flagpole
22. vice president
23. ninety-one
24. mangoes
25. sinews

© Macmillan/McGraw-Hill

At Home: Help the student practice the words he or she missed to prepare for the Posttest.

Name_____

Using the Word Study Steps

1. LOOK at the word.

2. SAY the word aloud.

3. STUDY the letters in the word.

4. WRITE the word.

5. CHECK the word.
   Did you spell the word right?
   If not, go back to step 1.

X the Words

Put an X on the one word in each line that does not fit the spelling pattern.

1. liberties	possibilities	zeroes	abilities
2. fangs	countries	rodeos	beliefs
3. batches	rattlers	reptiles	fangs
4. lashes	potatoes	identities	notches
5. difficulties	eddies	possibilities	rodeos
6. taxes	abilities	losses	notches
7. reptiles	batches	taxes	potatoes
8. beliefs	rodeos	rattlers	difficulties
9. countries	identities	surroundings	eddies
10. losses	zeroes	lashes	liberties

© Macmillan/McGraw-Hill

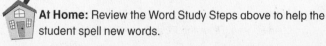

At Home: Review the Word Study Steps above to help the student spell new words.

Name_____

abilities	countries	batches	difficulties	eddies
fangs	identities	lashes	liberties	notches
possibilities	rattlers	reptiles	rodeos	surroundings
taxes	losses	potatoes	zeroes	beliefs

Pattern Power!

Sort the spelling words by finding the spelling pattern to which each belongs.

-es

1. _____
2. _____
3. _____
4. _____
5. _____
6. _____
7. _____

-s

1. _____
2. _____
3. _____
4. _____
5. _____

no change

1. _____

-ies

1. _____
2. _____
3. _____
4. _____
5. _____
6. _____
7. _____

© Macmillan/McGraw-Hill

abilities	countries	batches	difficulties	eddies
fangs	identities	lashes	liberties	notches
possibilities	rattlers	reptiles	rodeos	surroundings
taxes	losses	potatoes	zeroes	beliefs

Fill in the Blanks

Write the spelling word that best completes each sentence.

1. The water whirled around in the _____.

2. Rattlesnakes live in several _____ with different climates.

3. Miranda enjoyed making mashed _____ with gravy.

4. The spy had several different _____ to fool his enemies.

5. Snakes can be found at the zoo with other _____.

6. The number one million contains six _____.

7. Rattlers are more aware of their _____ than people are.

8. The team had ten wins and three _____ in the season.

Similar Meanings

Write the spelling word that has the same, or almost the same, meaning.

9. talents _____

10. freedoms _____

11. snakes _____

12. values _____

13. government money _____

14. snakes' teeth _____

15. cowboy entertainment _____

16. problems _____

17. eye protection _____

18. groups _____

19. suggestions _____

20. cuts _____

© Macmillan/McGraw-Hill

Name_____

Circle each misspelled word in this report. Write the correctly spelled word on the lines below.

Americans are asked to help their government according to their abilitys. In the United States, as in many other countreys, this means that people must pay taxs. The government uses the money to help citizens, build projects, and defend our libertyes. Sometimes paying the government causes difficultyes, especially if businesses have had losss during the year.

1. _____   3. _____   5. _____

2. _____   4. _____   6. _____

Writing Activity

Write a short report about snakes. Use four spelling words in your writing.

_____

_____

_____

_____

_____

_____

_____

_____

_____

_____

_____

_____

© Macmillan/McGraw-Hill

Name_____

Look at the words in each set below. One word in each set is spelled correctly. Use a pencil to fill in the circle next to the correct word. Before you begin, look at the sample set of words. Sample A has been done for you. Do Sample B by yourself. When you are sure you know what to do, you may go on with the rest of the page.

Sample A:
- Ⓐ scraches
- Ⓑ scratches
- Ⓒ skratches
- Ⓓ scratchis

Sample B:
- Ⓔ snakes
- Ⓕ snakies
- Ⓖ snaks
- Ⓗ snaiks

1. Ⓐ abilitys
   Ⓑ abilitees
   Ⓒ abilities
   Ⓓ abbilities

2. Ⓔ countries
   Ⓕ countrys
   Ⓖ contries
   Ⓗ countrees

3. Ⓐ batches
   Ⓑ batchs
   Ⓒ batchess
   Ⓓ baches

4. Ⓔ difficultys
   Ⓕ dificulties
   Ⓖ difficulties
   Ⓗ difficullties

5. Ⓐ eddys
   Ⓑ eddeys
   Ⓒ edies
   Ⓓ eddies

6. Ⓔ fangz
   Ⓕ fangs
   Ⓖ fanges
   Ⓗ fanegs

7. Ⓐ identitees
   Ⓑ identitys
   Ⓒ identities
   Ⓓ iddentities

8. Ⓔ lashes
   Ⓕ lashs
   Ⓖ lashus
   Ⓗ lasshes

9. Ⓐ libertees
   Ⓑ libberties
   Ⓒ libertys
   Ⓓ liberties

10. Ⓔ notchs
    Ⓕ notchas
    Ⓖ notches
    Ⓗ noches

11. Ⓐ possibilities
    Ⓑ possabilities
    Ⓒ posibilities
    Ⓓ possibleities

12. Ⓔ rattleres
    Ⓕ rattlers
    Ⓖ ratlers
    Ⓗ rattllers

13. Ⓐ reptyles
    Ⓑ reptils
    Ⓒ reptiles
    Ⓓ repptiles

14. Ⓔ rodeos
    Ⓕ rodeoes
    Ⓖ rodios
    Ⓗ rodeose

15. Ⓐ surroundings
    Ⓑ suroundings
    Ⓒ surrounddings
    Ⓓ surrounndings

16. Ⓔ taxs
    Ⓕ taxes
    Ⓖ tackses
    Ⓗ taxxes

17. Ⓐ lossses
    Ⓑ losssses
    Ⓒ losses
    Ⓓ lausses

18. Ⓔ pitatoes
    Ⓕ patatoes
    Ⓖ potaitoes
    Ⓗ potatoes

19. Ⓐ zerose
    Ⓑ zeroes
    Ⓒ zerros
    Ⓓ zerroes

20. Ⓔ beleafs
    Ⓕ beleefs
    Ⓖ beliefs
    Ⓗ biliefs

© Macmillan/McGraw-Hill

Name _____

Fold back the paper along the dotted line. Write the words in the blanks as they are read aloud. When you finish the test, unfold the paper. Use the list at the right to correct any spelling mistakes.

1. _____
2. _____
3. _____
4. _____
5. _____
6. _____
7. _____
8. _____
9. _____
10. _____
11. _____
12. _____
13. _____
14. _____
15. _____
16. _____
17. _____
18. _____
19. _____
20. _____

Review Words 21. _____

22. _____

23. _____

Challenge Words 24. _____

25. _____

1. jogging
2. dripping
3. skimmed
4. raking
5. amusing
6. easing
7. regretted
8. forbidding
9. referred
10. injured
11. deserved
12. applied
13. relied
14. renewing
15. complicated
16. qualified
17. threatening
18. gnarled
19. envied
20. fascinated
21. difficulties
22. notches
23. rodeos
24. adoring
25. diaries

At Home: Help the student practice the words he or she missed to prepare for the Posttest.

Maya Lin • **Grade 5/Unit 2** **45**

© Macmillan/McGraw-Hill

Name_____

Using the Word Study Steps

1. LOOK at the word.

2. SAY the word aloud.

3. STUDY the letters in the word.

4. WRITE the word.

5. CHECK the word.
   Did you spell the word right?
   If not, go back to step 1.

Find and Circle

Find and circle each of the spelling words in this puzzle. Words may read forward, backward, upward, or downward.

```
G Q A D S L F M R G D A R Z T J Y C
N U P E K F F A N E K B M G Q F O O
I A P I Y B S I T D E V R E S E D M
N L L V X I W A D E T T E R G E R P
E I I N V E N G N I K A R B G K D L
T F E E N I D R I P P I N G N G E I
A I D E C G N I S U M A S E A N M C
E E R S O I N J U R E D N A R I M A
R D A D E I L E R C O K G S L G I T
H F F O R B I D D I N G S I E G K E
T P R G D D E R R E F E R N D O S D
B L A G C P V Y R X Y Q N G S J Q R
```

List the words below as you find them in the puzzle.

1. _____   6. _____   11. _____   16. _____

2. _____   7. _____   12. _____   17. _____

3. _____   8. _____   13. _____   18. _____

4. _____   9. _____   14. _____   19. _____

5. _____   10. _____   15. _____   20. _____

At Home: Review the Word Study Steps above to help the student spell new words.

© Macmillan/McGraw-Hill

Name_____

qualified	renewing	skimmed	gnarled
threatening	envied	deserved	amusing
dripping	complicated	forbidding	relied
regretted	injured	applied	easing
raking	referred	jogging	fascinated

Sort each spelling word according to its ending. Write the spelling words that end in:

-ed

1. _____   7. _____

2. _____   8. _____

3. _____   9. _____

4. _____   10. _____

5. _____   11. _____

6. _____   12. _____

Write the spelling words that end in:

-ing

1. _____

2. _____

3. _____

4. _____

5. _____

6. _____

7. _____

8. _____

© Macmillan/McGraw-Hill

Name_____

qualified	renewing	skimmed	gnarled
threatening	envied	deserved	amusing
dripping	complicated	forbidding	relied
regretted	injured	applied	easing
raking	referred	jogging	fascinated

Definitions

Write the spelling word that has the same, or almost the same, meaning.

1. depended _____

2. amazed _____

3. funny _____

4. hard to understand or handle _____

5. hurt _____

6. running lightly _____

7. able; prepared for something _____

8. twisted; full of knots _____

9. read quickly _____

Sentence Completions

Complete each sentence with a spelling word.

10. The veterans of the Vietnam War _____ to have a monument built in their honor.

11. The family thought about _____ their membership to the museum.

12. Before a monument was built just for them, some women _____ the men.

13. The mural showed a woman _____ leaves outside her home.

14. Maya Lin _____ to the victims of the Civil War in her speech.

© Macmillan/McGraw-Hill

Name_____

Circle the misspelled words in the passage. Write the words correctly on the lines below.

Maya Lin stood there, getting ready to give her speech. She skimd her notes, making sure that nothing was missing. She had applide for the job three weeks ago, knowing that she was qualifide. Now that she worked at the museum, she regrettid not knowing about the job sooner. She began her speech with an amyusing story to relieve some of the pressure. Within minutes, the audience was fassinated.

1. _____   3. _____   5. _____

2. _____   4. _____   6. _____

Writing Activity

Write a paragraph about something you can do to honor those who have lost their lives in service to their country. Use four words from your spelling list.

_____

_____

_____

_____

_____

_____

_____

_____

_____

_____

_____

_____

© Macmillan/McGraw-Hill

Name_____

Look at the words in each set below. One word in each set is spelled correctly. Use a pencil to fill in the circle next to the correct word. Before you begin, look at the sample set of words. Sample A has been done for you. Do Sample B by yourself. When you are sure you know what to do, you may go on with the rest of the page.

Sample A:
Ⓐ runnning
Ⓑ runing
Ⓒ running
Ⓓ rhunning

Sample B:
Ⓔ amazed
Ⓕ umazed
Ⓖ ammazed
Ⓗ amazzed

1. Ⓐ amusing
Ⓑ ammusing
Ⓒ amussing
Ⓓ ammussing

2. Ⓔ applied
Ⓕ apllyed
Ⓖ aplied
Ⓗ appllied

3. Ⓐ complicatted
Ⓑ complikated
Ⓒ commplicated
Ⓓ complicated

4. Ⓔ daserved
Ⓕ diserved
Ⓖ deserved
Ⓗ desserved

5. Ⓐ driping
Ⓑ dripping
Ⓒ drippping
Ⓓ drihping

6. Ⓔ easing
Ⓕ easeing
Ⓖ eazing
Ⓗ eazeing

7. Ⓐ envyed
Ⓑ enveyed
Ⓒ envied
Ⓓ enveed

8. Ⓔ fascanated
Ⓕ facinated
Ⓖ fassinated
Ⓗ fascinated

9. Ⓐ forbidding
Ⓑ forbiding
Ⓒ forebidding
Ⓓ fourbidding

10. Ⓔ narled
Ⓕ gnarld
Ⓖ narld
Ⓗ gnarled

11. Ⓐ injured
Ⓑ enjured
Ⓒ injurd
Ⓓ ingerred

12. Ⓔ joggging
Ⓕ joging
Ⓖ jogging
Ⓗ joggeng

13. Ⓐ quallified
Ⓑ qualified
Ⓒ qualafied
Ⓓ qualefied

14. Ⓔ rakking
Ⓕ rakeing
Ⓖ raking
Ⓗ raiking

15. Ⓐ regretted
Ⓑ regreted
Ⓒ reggretted
Ⓓ rigretted

16. Ⓔ rilied
Ⓕ rellied
Ⓖ realied
Ⓗ relied

17. Ⓐ rinewing
Ⓑ rennewing
Ⓒ renewing
Ⓓ reneweing

18. Ⓔ skimmed
Ⓕ skimed
Ⓖ skimmd
Ⓗ scimmed

19. Ⓐ thretening
Ⓑ threatning
Ⓒ threataning
Ⓓ threatening

20. Ⓔ riferred
Ⓕ refered
Ⓖ referred
Ⓗ refurred

© Macmillan/McGraw-Hill

Name _____

Fold back the paper along the dotted line. Write the words in the blanks as they are read aloud. When you finish the test, unfold the paper. Use the list at the right to correct any spelling mistakes.

1. _____
2. _____
3. _____
4. _____
5. _____
6. _____
7. _____
8. _____
9. _____
10. _____
11. _____
12. _____
13. _____
14. _____
15. _____
16. _____
17. _____
18. _____
19. _____
20. _____

Review Words 21. _____
22. _____
23. _____
Challenge Words 24. _____
25. _____

1. joint
2. foul
3. coil
4. hoist
5. stout
6. dawdle
7. mouthful
8. counter
9. brought
10. bawl
11. fountain
12. sprawls
13. douse
14. clause
15. sprouts
16. cautious
17. turmoil
18. scrawny
19. foundation
20. turquoise
21. relied
22. forbidding
23. easing
24. buoyant
25. renown

© Macmillan/McGraw-Hill

 At Home: Help the student practice the words he or she missed to prepare for the Posttest.

Name _____

Using the Word Study Steps

1. LOOK at the word.

2. SAY the word aloud.

3. STUDY the letters in the word.

4. WRITE the word.

5. CHECK the word.
Did you spell the word right?
If not, go back to step 1.

Here and There

Circle the spelling words in this puzzle. Each word appears once.

```
B  J  F  O  U  N  D  A  T  I  O  N  F
R  M  O  U  T  H  F  U  L  N  M  R  O
O  L  U  T  U  R  Q  U  O  I  S  E  U
U  K  L  X  B  A  W  L  P  R  T  Q  N
G  J  C  A  U  T  I  O  U  S  O  B  T
H  O  I  S  T  W  E  R  T  B  U  H  A
T  I  C  P  U  H  X  D  H  A  T  Y  I
D  N  L  R  R  S  P  R  A  W  L  S  N
O  T  A  O  M  B  C  O  I  L  V  Z  G
U  A  U  U  O  C  O  U  N  T  E  R  H
S  B  S  T  I  N  S  C  R  A  W  N  Y
E  R  E  S  L  V  D  A  W  D  L  E  C
```

© Macmillan/McGraw-Hill

At Home: Review the Word Study Steps above to help the
student spell new words.

bawl	brought	cautious	counter
coil	foul	foundation	fountain
joint	mouthful	dawdle	sprawls
sprouts	turmoil	stout	hoist
clause	turquoise	douse	scrawny

Sort each spelling word by finding the sound and spelling pattern to which it belongs.

Write the words with the sound /ô/ spelled:

aw

1. _____
2. _____
3. _____
4. _____

au

1. _____
2. _____

ou

1. _____

Write the words with the /ou/ sound:

1. _____
2. _____
3. _____
4. _____
5. _____
6. _____
7. _____
8. _____

Write the words with the /oi/ sound:

1. _____
2. _____
3. _____
4. _____
5. _____

© Macmillan/McGraw-Hill

bawl	brought	cautious	counter
coil	foul	foundation	fountain
joint	mouthful	dawdle	sprawls
sprouts	turmoil	stout	hoist
clause	turquoise	douse	scrawny

Analogies

An analogy compares two pairs of words. It shows how two word pairs are similar. For example, up is to down as in is to out. Use spelling words to complete the analogies below.

1. **desk** is to **office** as _____ is to **store**

2. **hot** is to **cold** as **hurry** is to _____

3. **corner** is to **wall** as _____ is to **arm**

4. **shingle** is to **roof** as **brick** is to _____

5. **car** is to **metal** as **ring** is to _____

6. **sprinkle** is to **rain** as _____ is to **plants**

7. **took** is to **take** as _____ is to **bring**

8. **book** is to **paper** as _____ is to **water**

9. **house** is to **home** as **stretches** is to _____

10. **drawer** is to **dresser** as _____ is to **writing**

Antonyms

Write the spelling word that is the *opposite* of each word below.

11. dry _____

12. release _____

13. careless _____

14. small taste _____

15. slender _____

16. peace _____

17. enormous _____

18. laugh _____

19. drop _____

20. fair _____

© Macmillan/McGraw-Hill

Circle the misspelled words in this paragraph. Write the words correctly on the lines below.

Lupe loved to work in her island garden. She checked it every morning, looking for sprowts of vegetables and flowers. First she would douwse the plants with water. Then she sampled a mouthful of fresh tomatoes. She broght fresh flowers in and put them on the kitchen counter. Her grandmother taught her to take long-stemmed flowers and coyle them into a crown. Sometimes it was fun to daudle in the garden, and enjoy the sound of water in the fauntain.

1. _____ 3. _____ 5. _____

2. _____ 4. _____ 6. _____

Writing Activity

Can you imagine a beautiful park? Write a description of the park and what you might do there. Use four spelling words in your description.

_____

_____

_____

_____

_____

_____

_____

_____

_____

_____

© Macmillan/McGraw-Hill

Look at the words in each set below. One word in each set is spelled correctly. Use a pencil to fill in the circle next to the correct word. Before you begin, look at the sample set of words. Sample A has been done for you. Do Sample B by yourself. When you are sure you know what to do, you may go on with the rest of the page.

Sample A:

Ⓐ baut
Ⓑ bouht
Ⓒ bought
Ⓓ bawt

Sample B:

Ⓔ spoil
Ⓕ spoyl
Ⓖ spoile
Ⓗ spoyel

1. Ⓐ baull
Ⓑ baul
Ⓒ bawll
Ⓓ bawl

2. Ⓔ braut
Ⓕ brought
Ⓖ brouht
Ⓗ braught

3. Ⓐ cautious
Ⓑ caushious
Ⓒ cautieous
Ⓓ cawtious

4. Ⓔ cownter
Ⓕ caunter
Ⓖ counter
Ⓗ cowntir

5. Ⓐ coil
Ⓑ coyl
Ⓒ coyel
Ⓓ coile

6. Ⓔ faul
Ⓕ foul
Ⓖ foull
Ⓗ faull

7. Ⓐ foundashen
Ⓑ fowndation
Ⓒ foundation
Ⓓ foundatien

8. Ⓔ fowntain
Ⓕ fountain
Ⓖ founten
Ⓗ fownten

9. Ⓐ joint
Ⓑ joynt
Ⓒ gioint
Ⓓ goint

10. Ⓔ mouthfull
Ⓕ mauthful
Ⓖ mouthful
Ⓗ mowthful

11. Ⓐ dawdle
Ⓑ dawdel
Ⓒ daudle
Ⓓ daudlle

12. Ⓔ sprauls
Ⓕ sprawlz
Ⓖ sprawls
Ⓗ sprols

13. Ⓐ sprowtts
Ⓑ sproutts
Ⓒ sprowts
Ⓓ sprouts

14. Ⓔ turmoil
Ⓕ termoil
Ⓖ tirmoil
Ⓗ turmmoil

15. Ⓐ staut
Ⓑ stoute
Ⓒ stout
Ⓓ stoutt

16. Ⓔ hoyst
Ⓕ hoiset
Ⓖ hoiste
Ⓗ hoist

17. Ⓐ clause
Ⓑ claus
Ⓒ clauze
Ⓓ clauz

18. Ⓔ terquoise
Ⓕ turquoise
Ⓖ turquoyse
Ⓗ turquoize

19. Ⓐ dous
Ⓑ douce
Ⓒ dawse
Ⓓ douse

20. Ⓔ skrawny
Ⓕ skrawny
Ⓖ scrawny
Ⓗ schrawny

© Macmillan/McGraw-Hill

At Home: Have students underline the words and phrases that helped them figure out each word's meaning.

Fold back the paper along the dotted line. Write the words in the blanks as they are read aloud. When you finish the test, unfold the paper. Use the list at the right to correct any spelling mistakes.

1. _____
2. _____
3. _____
4. _____
5. _____
6. _____
7. _____
8. _____
9. _____
10. _____
11. _____
12. _____
13. _____
14. _____
15. _____
16. _____
17. _____
18. _____
19. _____
20. _____

Review Words 21. _____
22. _____
23. _____

Challenge Words 24. _____
25. _____

1. dentist
2. jogger
3. fifteen
4. flatter
5. mutter
6. mustang
7. absent
8. hollow
9. empire
10. blizzard
11. culture
12. goggles
13. summon
14. champion
15. kennel
16. valley
17. fragment
18. gallop
19. vulture
20. pigment
21. sprawls
22. sprouts
23. mouthful
24. clammy
25. hammock

© Macmillan/McGraw-Hill

At Home: Help the student practice the words he or she missed to prepare for the Posttest.

Black Cowboy, Wild Horses
Grade 5/Unit 2
57

Name_____

Using the Word Study Steps

1. LOOK at the word.

2. SAY the word aloud.

3. STUDY the letters in the word.

4. WRITE the word.

5. CHECK the word.
Did you spell the word right?
If not, go back to step 1.

Fill in the missing letters of each word to form a spelling word.

1. ke _____ _____ el

2. cha _____ _____ ion

3. vu _____ _____ ure

4. ho _____ _____ ow

5. a _____ _____ ent

6. mu _____ _____ er

7. mu _____ _____ ang

8. fla _____ _____ er

9. e _____ _____ ire

10. go _____ _____ les

11. pi _____ _____ ent

12. fra _____ _____ ent

13. va _____ _____ ey

14. cu _____ _____ ure

15. ga _____ _____ op

16. su _____ _____ on

17. bli _____ _____ ard

18. fi _____ _____ een

19. jo _____ _____ er

20. de _____ _____ ist

Use the spelling words above to write a poem of at least 4 lines.

21. _____

22. _____

23. _____

24. _____

At Home: Review the Word Study Steps above to help the student spell new words.

© Macmillan/McGraw-Hill

Name_____

absent	valley	pigment	blizzard
empire	mutter	goggles	fifteen
gallop	dentist	jogger	kennel
summon	champion	mustang	flatter
fragment	hollow	vulture	culture

This week's spelling words have double consonants between two vowels. Sort the words according to the spelling pattern for the double consonants between the vowels.

double consonant repeated

1. _____
2. _____
3. _____
4. _____
5. _____
6. _____
7. _____
8. _____
9. _____
10. _____

double consonants different

1. _____
2. _____
3. _____
4. _____
5. _____
6. _____
7. _____
8. _____
9. _____
10. _____

Alphabetical Order

Use the lines below to write the spelling words in alphabetical order.

1. _____
2. _____
3. _____
4. _____
5. _____

6. _____
7. _____
8. _____
9. _____
10. _____

11. _____
12. _____
13. _____
14. _____
15. _____

16. _____
17. _____
18. _____
19. _____
20. _____

© Macmillan/McGraw-Hill

Name_____

absent	valley	pigment	blizzard
empire	mutter	goggles	fifteen
gallop	dentist	jogger	kennel
summon	champion	mustang	flatter
fragment	hollow	vulture	culture

We Go Together

Write the spelling word that matches each clue below.

1. snow storm _____
2. run _____
3. winner _____
4. to praise _____
5. eye protection _____
6. between mountains _____
7. dog's home _____

8. empty inside _____
9. not here _____
10. bird of prey _____
11. small piece _____
12. color in paint _____
13. tooth doctor _____
14. wild horse _____

Complete the Sentence

Finish each sentence using a spelling word.

15. The ruler took great pride in his _____.

16. We could hear the unhappy child _____ under his breath.

17. The Greek _____ had wonderful art and architecture.

18. My mother runs to stay healthy; she is a _____.

19. A judge can _____ you to be in court.

20. There will be _____ candles on her birthday cake.

© Macmillan/McGraw-Hill

Circle each incorrectly spelled word in this diary entry. Write the words correctly on the lines below.

I like to read about the old West. There are great stories about the cullture of the ranchers and cowboys. I like to imagine what it would be like to galop away on a mustang. Cowboys and cowgirls faced danger often. They could be lost in a valey or caught in a blizzerd. Even in a safe place, they could be hurt by a fragmment of stone thrown from a horse's hoof. The wide and empty range must have felt like the cowboy's emmpire.

1. _____   3. _____   5. _____

2. _____   4. _____   6. _____

Writing Activity

Write a letter to Bob or another cowboy or cowgirl. Use four words from the spelling list.

_____

_____

_____

_____

_____

_____

_____

_____

_____

_____

_____

© Macmillan/McGraw-Hill

Name_____

Look at the words in each set below. One word in each set is spelled correctly. Use a pencil to fill in the circle next to the correct word. Before you begin, look at the sample set of words. Sample A has been done for you. Do Sample B by yourself. When you are sure you know what to do, you may go on with the rest of the page.

Sample A:

- Ⓐ umpirre
- Ⓑ ummpire
- Ⓒ umpyre
- Ⓓ umpire

Sample B:

- Ⓔ scalop
- Ⓕ scallop
- Ⓖ scalllop
- Ⓗ scallup

1. Ⓐ abssent
   Ⓑ absint
   Ⓒ abbsent
   Ⓓ absent

2. Ⓔ vallee
   Ⓕ valley
   Ⓖ vallie
   Ⓗ valey

3. Ⓐ pigment
   Ⓑ pigmint
   Ⓒ piggment
   Ⓓ pigmunt

4. Ⓔ blizzard
   Ⓕ blissard
   Ⓖ blizard
   Ⓗ blisard

5. Ⓐ emppire
   Ⓑ empeir
   Ⓒ empyre
   Ⓓ empire

6. Ⓔ muttter
   Ⓕ mutter
   Ⓖ muttar
   Ⓗ muttur

7. Ⓐ goggles
   Ⓑ gogles
   Ⓒ ghoggles
   Ⓓ goggels

8. Ⓔ fivteen
   Ⓕ fifteen
   Ⓖ fiftene
   Ⓗ fiffteen

9. Ⓐ gallup
   Ⓑ galop
   Ⓒ ghallop
   Ⓓ gallop

10. Ⓔ denttist
    Ⓕ dentisst
    Ⓖ dentist
    Ⓗ denntist

11. Ⓐ joger
    Ⓑ jogger
    Ⓒ joggerr
    Ⓓ joggir

12. Ⓔ kennal
    Ⓕ kennul
    Ⓖ kennel
    Ⓗ kennle

13. Ⓐ summun
    Ⓑ summonn
    Ⓒ sumon
    Ⓓ summon

14. Ⓔ champion
    Ⓕ champyon
    Ⓖ champeon
    Ⓗ champiun

15. Ⓐ musttang
    Ⓑ musstang
    Ⓒ mustang
    Ⓓ mustange

16. Ⓔ flater
    Ⓕ flatter
    Ⓖ flattur
    Ⓗ flattar

17. Ⓐ fragment
    Ⓑ fragmint
    Ⓒ fragmunt
    Ⓓ fraggment

18. Ⓔ holow
    Ⓕ haullow
    Ⓖ hollo
    Ⓗ hollow

19. Ⓐ vulture
    Ⓑ vulchure
    Ⓒ vultire
    Ⓓ vulcher

20. Ⓔ culcher
    Ⓕ culchure
    Ⓖ culture
    Ⓗ cullture

© Macmillan/McGraw-Hill

Name_____

Read each sentence. If an underlined word is spelled wrong, fill in the circle that goes with that word. If no word is spelled wrong, fill in the circle below NONE. Read Sample A and do Sample B.

NONE

A. The loud soond came from a high tower.
          A   B   C

A. Ⓐ ● Ⓒ Ⓓ

NONE

B. The grate big balloon burst with a bang.
          E   F   G

B. Ⓔ Ⓕ Ⓖ Ⓗ

NONE

1. This afternoon I saw an earthworm crawling through
              A   B

cornmeil.
    C

1. Ⓐ Ⓑ Ⓒ Ⓓ

NONE

2. Beautiful turquise water filled a fifteen foot fountain.
                  E   F   G

2. Ⓔ Ⓕ Ⓖ Ⓗ

NONE

3. Let's galop into the valley for shelter from the blizzard.
              A   B   C

3. Ⓐ Ⓑ Ⓒ Ⓓ

NONE

4. Some reptiles, including ratlers, have fangs.
              E   F   G

4. Ⓔ Ⓕ Ⓖ Ⓗ

NONE

5. She brought a coil of rope into the vally.
              A   B   C

5. Ⓐ Ⓑ Ⓒ Ⓓ

NONE

6. From the rooftop, I could see a valture in our cornfield.
                  E   F   G

6. Ⓔ Ⓕ Ⓖ Ⓗ

NONE

7. People find reptiles amuseing in some countries.
                  A   B   C

7. Ⓐ Ⓑ Ⓒ Ⓓ

NONE

8. In the field, she was fascinated by the eartworm and
                              E   F

the vulture.
        G

8. Ⓔ Ⓕ Ⓖ Ⓗ

NONE

9. Amusing things happened in all of the fifteen countrys
          A   B   C

we visited.

9. Ⓐ Ⓑ Ⓒ Ⓓ

NONE

10. Who brught fifteen reptiles to the zoo?
                E   F   G

10. Ⓔ Ⓕ Ⓖ Ⓗ

© Macmillan/McGraw-Hill

Name_____

11. He saw an <u>egshell</u> this <u>afternoon</u>, not an <u>earthworm</u>.
                A   B   C

NONE
11. Ⓐ Ⓑ Ⓒ Ⓓ

12. The <u>foundation</u> of the <u>fontain</u> is <u>dripping</u> wet.
             E   F   G

NONE
12. Ⓔ Ⓕ Ⓖ Ⓗ

13. A piece of turquoise <u>eggshell</u> fell from the <u>roofop</u> nest.
               A   B   C

NONE
13. Ⓐ Ⓑ Ⓒ Ⓓ

14. That <u>afternon</u>, we <u>regretted</u> using all of the <u>cornmeal</u>.
          E   F   G

NONE
14. Ⓔ Ⓕ Ⓖ Ⓗ

15. We had <u>difficultes</u> <u>amusing</u> our cousin all <u>afternoon</u>.
           A   B   C

NONE
15. Ⓐ Ⓑ Ⓒ Ⓓ

16. We piled <u>potatoes</u> and <u>sprouts</u> on the kitchen <u>conter</u>.
          E   F   G

NONE
16. Ⓔ Ⓕ Ⓖ Ⓗ

17. The <u>blizard</u> over the <u>valley</u> <u>fascinated</u> me.
          A   B   C

NONE
17. Ⓐ Ⓑ Ⓒ Ⓓ

18. I've seen <u>rattlers</u> in that <u>holow</u> log by the <u>cornfield</u>.
            E   F   G

NONE
18. Ⓔ Ⓕ Ⓖ Ⓗ

19. The <u>blizzard</u> <u>complicaten</u> our <u>field trip</u> plans.
          A   B   C

NONE
19. Ⓐ Ⓑ Ⓒ Ⓓ

20. The dog was <u>fascinatid</u> by the <u>hollow</u> log in the <u>valley</u>.
             E   F   G

NONE
20. Ⓔ Ⓕ Ⓖ Ⓗ

21. A snake will <u>coyl</u> and show its <u>fangs</u> in a <u>blizzard</u>.
              A   B   C

NONE
21. Ⓐ Ⓑ Ⓒ Ⓓ

22. <u>Rattlers</u> with <u>fanges</u> create <u>difficulties</u> for cowhands.
   E   F   G

NONE
22. Ⓔ Ⓕ Ⓖ Ⓗ

23. The patient horse <u>deservid</u> a <u>gallop</u> through the <u>valley</u>.
                  A   B   C

NONE
23. Ⓐ Ⓑ Ⓒ Ⓓ

24. He <u>deserved</u> a break after the <u>complicated</u> <u>counter</u>
     E   F   G
situation.

NONE
24. Ⓔ Ⓕ Ⓖ Ⓗ

25. She <u>regrettid</u> bringing the <u>cornmeal</u> and the <u>eggshell</u>.
       A   B   C

NONE
25. Ⓐ Ⓑ Ⓒ Ⓓ

© Macmillan/McGraw-Hill

Name_____

Fold back the paper along the dotted line. Write the words in the blanks as they are read aloud. When you finish the test, unfold the paper. Use the list at the right to correct any spelling mistakes.

1. _____
2. _____
3. _____
4. _____
5. _____
6. _____
7. _____
8. _____
9. _____
10. _____
11. _____
12. _____
13. _____
14. _____
15. _____
16. _____
17. _____
18. _____
19. _____
20. _____

Review Words 21. _____

22. _____

23. _____

Challenge Words 24. _____

25. _____

1. minus
2. loser
3. humor
4. closet
5. recent
6. student
7. equal
8. profile
9. local
10. comet
11. vacant
12. punish
13. cavern
14. shiver
15. decent
16. linen
17. legal
18. panic
19. smoky
20. tyrant
21. valley
22. fifteen
23. culture
24. fatigue
25. fugitive

© Macmillan/McGraw-Hill

At Home: Help the student practice the words he or she missed to prepare for the Posttest.

Sleds on Boston Common

Grade 5/Unit 3

65

Name_____

Using the Word Study Steps

1. LOOK at the word.

2. SAY the word aloud.

3. STUDY the letters in the word.

4. WRITE the word.

5. CHECK the word.
Did you spell the word right?
If not, go back to step 1.

Find and Circle

Where are the spelling words?

l i n e n c j g l e g a l w p x s t u d e n t h u m o r t u h o
b r d c a v e r n e m i n u s b z t p r o f i l e e t l e q u a l
p u n i s h t o m t y r a n t e y y s m o k y u a t r e c e n t
g i s v a c a n t h p a n i c m u c l o c a l b z t s h i v e r
c o m e t h w v l o s e r f t r d e c e n t l o k c l o s e t e r

List the words below as you find them in the puzzle.

1. _____   6. _____   11. _____   16. _____

2. _____   7. _____   12. _____   17. _____

3. _____   8. _____   13. _____   18. _____

4. _____   9. _____   14. _____   19. _____

5. _____   10. _____   15. _____   20. _____

At Home: Review the Word Study Steps above to help the student spell new words.

© Macmillan/McGraw-Hill

Name _____

tyrant	profile	smoky	minus	local
equal	linen	legal	loser	decent
humor	closet	comet	punish	vacant
recent	student	shiver	cavern	panic

Sort each spelling word by determining if it follows the V/VC pattern or the VC/V pattern. Write each word in the correct column.

V/CV Pattern

1. _____
2. _____
3. _____
4. _____
5. _____
6. _____
7. _____
8. _____
9. _____
10. _____
11. _____
12. _____
13. _____

VC/V Pattern

1. _____
2. _____
3. _____
4. _____
5. _____
6. _____
7. _____

Use the spelling words above to help you write a poem of at least 4 lines.

1. _____
2. _____
3. _____
4. _____

© Macmillan/McGraw-Hill

Name_____

tyrant	profile	smoky	minus	local
equal	linen	legal	loser	decent
humor	closet	comet	punish	vacant
recent	student	shiver	cavern	panic

Definitions

Write the spelling word that matches each definition below.

1. bully _____

2. empty _____

3. cavern _____

4. one who lost _____

5. type of cloth _____

6. place for clothes _____

7. pupil _____

8. the same as _____

9. subtract _____

10. shake _____

Finish the Sentences

Write the spelling word that best completes each sentence.

11. Do you think the general would _____ the children for speaking to him?

12. I was frightened, but I didn't _____ when I saw the soldiers.

13. The general laughed at him, so he must have had a sense of

_____.

14. If you're looking at his _____, you're looking at the side of his face.

15. Was that a _____ event, or did it happen a long time ago?

16. They wondered if the laws that he passed were _____.

17. The soldiers had been smoking a pipe, so the room was _____.

18. The _____ streaked through the night sky.

19. The _____ pond closest to our house was full of ice.

20. They came to believe that the general was a _____ man.

© Macmillan/McGraw-Hill

Name

Circle the misspelled words in this paragraph. Write the words correctly on the lines below.

Colin felt that General Gage was a desent man, and not a tierant like King George. General Gage understood that a studdent like Colin enjoyed sledding on a locall hill during recess. General Gage didn't even punnish Colin for being so bold in asking him to remove the tents from the hill. Even though the cold wind made Colin shivver, he was happy that General Gage had made it possible to go sledding

1. _____   3. _____   5. _____

2. _____   4. _____   6. _____

Writing Activity

Think about something that you like to do. Has there ever been a time when you couldn't do it and you had to ask someone's permission to help you? Write about what happened, or what you think might happen, in this situation. Use four spelling words.

_____

_____

_____

_____

_____

_____

_____

_____

_____

_____

_____

© Macmillan/McGraw-Hill

Name_____

Look at the words in each set below. One word in each set is spelled correctly. Use a pencil to fill in the circle next to the correct word. Before you begin, look at the sample set of words. Sample A has been done for you. Do Sample B by yourself. When you are sure you know what to do, you may go on with the rest of the page.

Sample A:

Ⓐ regu
Ⓑ regal
Ⓒ reagel
Ⓓ reagal

Sample B:

Ⓔ closee
Ⓕ closser
Ⓖ cloeser
Ⓗ closer

1. Ⓐ tyrunt
Ⓑ tyrent
Ⓒ tirant
Ⓓ tyrant

2. Ⓔ profyle
Ⓕ proffile
Ⓖ profile
Ⓗ profille

3. Ⓐ smoky
Ⓑ smmoky
Ⓒ smokky
Ⓓ smokkey

4. Ⓔ mihnus
Ⓕ minus
Ⓖ minis
Ⓗ mineus

5. Ⓐ local
Ⓑ lockal
Ⓒ locul
Ⓓ locel

6. Ⓔ equel
Ⓕ equul
Ⓖ equal
Ⓗ equall

7. Ⓐ linnen
Ⓑ linen
Ⓒ lynen
Ⓓ lynnen

8. Ⓔ legal
Ⓕ legul
Ⓖ legall
Ⓗ leegal

9. Ⓐ lozer
Ⓑ loozer
Ⓒ loseer
Ⓓ loser

10. Ⓔ decent
Ⓕ deesent
Ⓖ desent
Ⓗ descint

11. Ⓐ houmor
Ⓑ huemor
Ⓒ humor
Ⓓ humer

12. Ⓔ closset
Ⓕ closet
Ⓖ clozet
Ⓗ closett

13. Ⓐ comet
Ⓑ commet
Ⓒ comit
Ⓓ comett

14. Ⓔ punissh
Ⓕ punnish
Ⓖ punish
Ⓗ puhnish

15. Ⓐ vacent
Ⓑ vaceant
Ⓒ vaccant
Ⓓ vacant

16. Ⓔ recent
Ⓕ rescent
Ⓖ ricent
Ⓗ resint

17. Ⓐ student
Ⓑ stoodent
Ⓒ studint
Ⓓ studdent

18. Ⓔ shivver
Ⓕ schiver
Ⓖ shiver
Ⓗ shivur

19. Ⓐ cavirn
Ⓑ cavurn
Ⓒ cavern
Ⓓ cavvern

20. Ⓔ pannick
Ⓕ pannic
Ⓖ panick
Ⓗ panic

© Macmillan/McGraw-Hill

Name _____

Fold back the paper along the dotted line. Write the words in the blanks as they are read aloud. When you finish the test, unfold the paper. Use the list at the right to correct any spelling mistakes.

1. _____
2. _____
3. _____
4. _____
5. _____
6. _____
7. _____
8. _____
9. _____
10. _____
11. _____
12. _____
13. _____
14. _____
15. _____
16. _____
17. _____
18. _____
19. _____
20. _____

Review Words
21. _____
22. _____
23. _____

Challenge Words
24. _____
25. _____

1. video
2. poet
3. riot
4. piano
5. diary
6. radio
7. ideas
8. ruin
9. diet
10. patriot
11. fluid
12. rodeo
13. cruel
14. genuine
15. casual
16. trial
17. fuel
18. meteor
19. diameter
20. meander
21. recent
22. closet
23. minus
24. situation
25. variety

At Home: Help the student practice the words he or she missed to prepare for the Posttest.

© Macmillan/McGraw-Hill

Name_____

Using the Word Study Steps

1. LOOK at the word.

2. SAY the word aloud.

3. STUDY the letters in the word.

4. WRITE the word.

5. CHECK the word.
   Did you spell the word right?
   If not, go back to step 1.

Fill-Ins

Fill in the missing letters of each word to form a spelling word.

1. cas ____ ____ l

2. rod ____ ____

3. rad ____ ____

4. p ____ ____ t

5. d ____ ____ meter

6. r ____ ____ n

7. vid ____ ____

8. p ____ ____ no

9. cr ____ ____ l

10. met ____ ____ r

11. gen ____ ____ ne

12. fl ____ ____ d

13. d ____ ____ ry

14. id ____ ____ s

15. patr ____ ____ t

16. f ____ ____ l

17. d ____ ____ t

18. r ____ ____ t

19. tr ____ ____ l

20. m ____ ____ nder

Reverse Alphabetical Order

Use the lines below to write the spelling words in reverse alphabetical order.

1. _____
2. _____
3. _____
4. _____
5. _____
6. _____
7. _____
8. _____
9. _____
10. _____
11. _____
12. _____
13. _____
14. _____
15. _____
16. _____
17. _____
18. _____
19. _____
20. _____

© Macmillan/McGraw-Hill

At Home: Review the Word Study Steps above to help the student spell new words.

Name_____

ideas	piano	fuel	casual	meander
poet	diary	rodeo	trial	genuine
riot	radio	meteor	diet	diameter
video	fluid	cruel	ruin	patriot

Sort each spelling word by finding the sound and spelling pattern to which it belongs.

ea

1. _____
2. _____

eo

1. _____
2. _____
3. _____

ia

1. _____
2. _____
3. _____
4. _____

ie

1. _____

io

1. _____
2. _____
3. _____

oe

1. _____

ua

1. _____

ue

1. _____
2. _____

ui

1. _____
2. _____
3. _____

© Macmillan/McGraw-Hill

Name_____

ideas	piano	fuel	casual	meander
poet	diary	rodeo	trial	genuine
riot	radio	meteor	diet	diameter
video	fluid	cruel	ruin	patriot

Fill in the Blank

Write the spelling word that best completes each sentence.

1. Esther wrote in her _____ each day.

2. Did you watch the _____ about voting rights?

3. She played the _____ while he sang.

4. Did all the angry people looking for gold cause a _____?

5. Her _____ included the belief that women should be able to vote and hold office.

6. I'd like to write a poem about her, but I am not a _____.

7. We went to Wyoming and saw horses and cowboys at the _____.

8. The horses had a _____ of oats and other grains.

9. The cowboys were not _____. They treated the horses kindly.

10. We wore _____ clothing because we were sitting on the ground.

Definitions

Write the spelling word that matches each definition below.

11. device that plays music and news _____

12. real, not fake _____

13. line through the center of a circle _____

14. move or walk slowly _____

15. one who supports his or her country _____

16. rock from space _____

17. type of energy, such as gasoline _____

18. destroy _____

19. decision process in a court _____

20. liquid _____

© Macmillan/McGraw-Hill

Name_____

Circle the misspelled words in the passage. Write the words correctly on the lines below.

     Mrs. Esther Morris was a true patreot. In her time, she would have been called a genuen article. She was a fair judge. She didn't punish Ben Sheeks when he misbehaved during a tryial. There was no vidio when Mrs. Morris lived. There wasn't even radeo. I would have liked to see or hear her. I like many of her ideus.

1. _____   3. _____   5. _____

2. _____   4. _____   6. _____

Writing Activity

Suppose that you could write a letter to Mrs. Morris. What would you say about her ideas? How would you describe what voting is like today? Use the lines below to write your letter. Include four spelling words.

_____

_____

_____

_____

_____

_____

_____

_____

_____

_____

© Macmillan/McGraw-Hill

Look at the words in each set below. One word in each set is spelled correctly. Use a pencil to fill in the circle next to the correct word. Before you begin, look at the sample set of words. Sample A has been done for you. Do Sample B by yourself. When you are sure you know what to do, you may go on with the rest of the page.

Sample A:

Ⓐ dial
Ⓑ diul
Ⓒ dieal
Ⓓ diel

Sample B:

Ⓔ audieo
Ⓕ audio
Ⓖ audeo
Ⓗ auddio

1. Ⓐ ideas
   Ⓑ idees
   Ⓒ ideaz
   Ⓓ iddeas

2. Ⓔ poett
   Ⓕ poete
   Ⓖ poet
   Ⓗ poette

3. Ⓐ ryot
   Ⓑ riot
   Ⓒ riott
   Ⓓ rhiot

4. Ⓔ viddeo
   Ⓕ vidio
   Ⓖ vidieo
   Ⓗ video

5. Ⓐ piano
   Ⓑ pianno
   Ⓒ peano
   Ⓓ peanno

6. Ⓔ diery
   Ⓕ dieary
   Ⓖ diary
   Ⓗ dyary

7. Ⓐ radio
   Ⓑ radeo
   Ⓒ radieo
   Ⓓ raidio

8. Ⓔ flewid
   Ⓕ flued
   Ⓖ flooid
   Ⓗ fluid

9. Ⓐ jenuine
   Ⓑ genuine
   Ⓒ genuin
   Ⓓ genuinne

10. Ⓔ rodeo
    Ⓕ rodio
    Ⓖ rodeio
    Ⓗ roddeo

11. Ⓐ meteur
    Ⓑ meeteor
    Ⓒ meteor
    Ⓓ metior

12. Ⓔ crewl
    Ⓕ crule
    Ⓖ cruel
    Ⓗ cruell

13. Ⓐ casual
    Ⓑ cassual
    Ⓒ casuall
    Ⓓ cazual

14. Ⓔ meandir
    Ⓕ meannder
    Ⓖ meander
    Ⓗ meandar

15. Ⓐ diammeter
    Ⓑ dyameter
    Ⓒ dieameter
    Ⓓ diameter

16. Ⓔ fuel
    Ⓕ fuell
    Ⓖ fule
    Ⓗ fewl

17. Ⓐ paitriot
    Ⓑ patriot
    Ⓒ paytriot
    Ⓓ patriet

18. Ⓔ rhuin
    Ⓕ ruine
    Ⓖ ruin
    Ⓗ rooin

19. Ⓐ diet
    Ⓑ diete
    Ⓒ diett
    Ⓓ dyet

20. Ⓔ triel
    Ⓕ trial
    Ⓖ triall
    Ⓗ tryal

© Macmillan/McGraw-Hill

Name_____

Fold back the paper along the dotted line. Write the words in the blanks as they are read aloud. When you finish the test, unfold the paper. Use the list at the right to correct any spelling mistakes.

Review Words

Challenge Words

1. _____
2. _____
3. _____
4. _____
5. _____
6. _____
7. _____
8. _____
9. _____
10. _____
11. _____
12. _____
13. _____
14. _____
15. _____
16. _____
17. _____
18. _____
19. _____
20. _____
21. _____
22. _____
23. _____
24. _____
25. _____

1. hilltop
2. grassland
3. footprint
4. handsome
5. landlord
6. partner
7. cockpit
8. fairground
9. address
10. fiddler
11. reckless
12. pilgrim
13. improve
14. instant
15. dolphin
16. orphan
17. concrete
18. complain
19. district
20. although
21. ideas
22. piano
23. fuel
24. mischief
25. laughter

© Macmillan/McGraw-Hill

At Home: Help the student practice the words he or she missed to prepare for the Posttest.

Name_____

Using the Word Study Steps

1. LOOK at the word.

2. SAY the word aloud.

3. STUDY the letters in the word.

4. WRITE the word.

5. CHECK the word.
    Did you spell the word right?
    If not, go back to step 1.

Fill-Ins

Fill in the missing letters of each word to form a spelling word.

1. a _____ _____ _____ ough

2. di _____ _____ _____ ict

3. gra _____ _____ _____ and

4. la _____ _____ _____ ord

5. ha _____ _____ _____ ome

6. a _____ _____ _____ ess

7. co _____ _____ _____ ete

8. i _____ _____ _____ ant

9. co _____ _____ _____ ain

10. o _____ _____ _____ an

11. i _____ _____ _____ ove

12. re _____ _____ _____ ess

13. pi _____ _____ _____ im

14. pa _____ _____ _____ er

15. foo _____ _____ _____ int

16. fi _____ _____ _____ er

17. do _____ _____ _____ in

18. fai _____ _____ _____ ound

19. hi _____ _____ _____ op

20. co _____ _____ _____ it

Make a Puzzle

Make a puzzle of your own using the space on this page. Give it to someone else to solve. Be sure to include at least five spelling words in your puzzle.

© Macmillan/McGraw-Hill

At Home: Review the Word Study Steps above to help the
student spell new words.

Name _____

orphan	complain	hilltop	concrete
instant	reckless	handsome	fairground
grassland	landlord	pilgrim	district
address	improve	although	partner
footprint	dolphin	cockpit	fiddler

**Sort each spelling word by writing it in the correct column.
Note: One word can be placed in all three columns.**

First syllable is stressed

1. _____   9. _____

2. _____   10. _____

3. _____   11. _____

4. _____   12. _____

5. _____   13. _____

6. _____   14. _____

7. _____   15. _____

8. _____   16. _____

Second syllable is stressed

1. _____

2. _____

3. _____

4. _____

Either syllable could be stressed

1. _____

© Macmillan/McGraw-Hill

Name

orphan	complain	hilltop	concrete
instant	reckless	handsome	fairground
grassland	landlord	pilgrim	district
address	improve	although	partner
footprint	dolphin	cockpit	fiddler

Fill in the Blank

Write the spelling word that best completes each sentence.

1. A child who does not have parents is called an _____.

2. The _____ is a very intelligent marine animal.

3. Did the ranger _____ when they created their own path?

4. The _____ asked for the rent.

5. I'll meet you at the Ferris wheel in the _____.

6. Write your return _____ at the top of the letter.

7. My dance _____ didn't make a mistake during the recital.

8. The pilot sits in the airplane's _____.

Similar Meanings

Write the spelling word that has the same, or almost the same, meaning.

9. immediate _____

10. attractive _____

11. out of control _____

12. area _____

13. make better _____

14. one who plays a fiddle _____

15. grass-covered land _____

16. mixture of cement, sand, rock and water _____

© Macmillan/McGraw-Hill

Name_____

Circle the misspelled words in the passage. Write the words correctly on the lines below.

Althogh much has been done to protect the environment from rekless activities, there are many things that we can do to impruve our surroundings. My school has an environmental club. A local business is our pardner. We are raising money to restore a nearby grasland. We don't want it covered in concreet someday.

1. _____   3. _____   5. _____

2. _____   4. _____   6. _____

Writing Activity

Write a paragraph about an area near your home or school that you would like to protect. Use four words from your spelling list.

_____

_____

_____

_____

_____

_____

_____

_____

_____

_____

_____

_____

© Macmillan/McGraw-Hill

Look at the words in each set below. One word in each set is spelled correctly. Use a pencil to fill in the circle next to the correct word. Before you begin, look at the sample set of words. Sample A has been done for you. Do Sample B by yourself. When you are sure you know what to do, you may go on with the rest of the page.

Sample A:

- Ⓐ laffter
- Ⓑ lafter
- Ⓒ laughter
- Ⓓ laughtir

Sample B:

- Ⓔ complete
- Ⓕ compleet
- Ⓖ commplete
- Ⓗ compliet

1. Ⓐ orphen
   Ⓑ orphan
   Ⓒ orphun
   Ⓓ orphon

2. Ⓔ complain
   Ⓕ complane
   Ⓖ commplain
   Ⓗ complainn

3. Ⓐ hiltop
   Ⓑ hilltop
   Ⓒ hilltopp
   Ⓓ hillttop

4. Ⓔ concrete
   Ⓕ concreet
   Ⓖ concret
   Ⓗ concreat

5. Ⓐ instent
   Ⓑ instunt
   Ⓒ instant
   Ⓓ instont

6. Ⓔ reckluss
   Ⓕ reckliss
   Ⓖ reckless
   Ⓗ wreckless

7. Ⓐ handsomme
   Ⓑ handsum
   Ⓒ hansome
   Ⓓ handsome

8. Ⓔ faerground
   Ⓕ fairground
   Ⓖ fairgraund
   Ⓗ fareground

9. Ⓐ grasland
   Ⓑ grasslend
   Ⓒ grassland
   Ⓓ grasslland

10. Ⓔ landlord
    Ⓕ landdlord
    Ⓖ landlordd
    Ⓗ lanndlord

11. Ⓐ pilgrem
    Ⓑ pilgrim
    Ⓒ pillgrim
    Ⓓ pilgrum

12. Ⓔ districkt
    Ⓕ disstrict
    Ⓖ district
    Ⓗ distrikt

13. Ⓐ address
    Ⓑ adress
    Ⓒ addres
    Ⓓ adruss

14. Ⓔ impruev
    Ⓕ improov
    Ⓖ impruve
    Ⓗ improve

15. Ⓐ allthow
    Ⓑ althow
    Ⓒ although
    Ⓓ allthough

16. Ⓔ partner
    Ⓕ partener
    Ⓖ pardner
    Ⓗ partnir

17. Ⓐ footpprint
    Ⓑ futtprint
    Ⓒ foottprint
    Ⓓ footprint

18. Ⓔ dollphin
    Ⓕ dolffin
    Ⓖ dolphin
    Ⓗ dolfin

19. Ⓐ cockpit
    Ⓑ cokpit
    Ⓒ cockpitt
    Ⓓ cackpit

20. Ⓔ fidler
    Ⓕ fiddler
    Ⓖ fidller
    Ⓗ fiddleer

© Macmillan/McGraw-Hill

Name_____

Fold back the paper along the dotted line. Write the words in the blanks as they are read aloud. When you finish the test, unfold the paper. Use the list at the right to correct any spelling mistakes.

1. _____
2. _____
3. _____
4. _____
5. _____
6. _____
7. _____
8. _____
9. _____
10. _____
11. _____
12. _____
13. _____
14. _____
15. _____
16. _____
17. _____
18. _____
19. _____
20. _____

Review Words 21. _____

22. _____

23. _____

Challenge Words 24. _____

25. _____

1. dozen
2. beside
3. motion
4. appoint
5. season
6. phony
7. observe
8. active
9. restore
10. expert
11. reserve
12. embrace
13. coastal
14. python
15. govern
16. scorching
17. flurry
18. canvas
19. copper
20. cocoon
21. partner
22. footprint
23. dolphin
24. superb
25. bleachers

© Macmillan/McGraw-Hill

At Home: Help the student practice the words he or she missed to prepare for the Posttest.

Great-Grandmother's Gourd

83

Grade 5/Unit 3

Name_____

Using the Word Study Steps

1. LOOK at the word.

2. SAY the word aloud.

3. STUDY the letters in the word.

4. WRITE the word.

5. CHECK the word.
   Did you spell the word right?
   If not, go back to step 1.

Fill-Ins

Fill in the missing letters of each word to form a spelling word.

1. p _____ th _____ n

2. sc _____ rch _____ ng

3. s _____ _____ son

4. d _____ z _____ n

5. m _____ ti _____ n

6. ph _____ n _____

7. _____ ct _____ ve

8. c _____ nv _____ s

9. _____ xp _____ rt

10. _____ mbr _____ ce

11. c _____ _____ stal

12. r _____ s _____ rve

13. g _____ v _____ rn

14. fl _____ rr _____

15. c _____ pp _____ r

16. app _____ _____ nt

17. b _____ s _____ de

18. c _____ c _____ _____ n

19. r _____ st _____ re

20. _____ bs _____ rve

Write the Words

Use the lines below to practice writing the spelling words.

_____ _____ _____ _____

_____ _____ _____ _____

_____ _____ _____ _____

_____ _____ _____ _____

_____ _____ _____ _____

Great-Grandmother's Gourd
Grade 5/Unit 3

 At Home: Review the Word Study Steps above to help the
student spell new words.

© Macmillan/McGraw-Hill

Name_____

scorching	reserve	coastal	phony
motion	dozen	beside	cocoon
appoint	python	restore	embrace
expert	canvas	season	observe
copper	flurry	govern	active

Write the spelling words in alphabetical order.

1. _____

2. _____

3. _____

4. _____

5. _____

6. _____

7. _____

8. _____

9. _____

10. _____

11. _____

12. _____

13. _____

14. _____

15. _____

16. _____

17. _____

18. _____

19. _____

20. _____

Make a Puzzle

Make a puzzle of your own using the space on this page. Give it to someone else to solve. Be sure to include at least five spelling words in your puzzle.

© Macmillan/McGraw-Hill

Name_____

scorching	reserve	coastal	phony
motion	dozen	beside	cocoon
appoint	python	restore	embrace
expert	canvas	season	observe
copper	flurry	govern	active

Fill in the Blank

Complete each sentence with a spelling word.

1. It was a hot day, and the sun was _____ the land.

2. The people in the village came running to stand _____ the new pump.

3. They thought it would be wise to _____ a leader to be in charge of the pump.

4. There must have been a _____ people lined up to try out the new machine.

5. Fatima made the pump work by using a smooth, pulling _____.

6. There was a _____ of activity, and then a gush of clear water.

7. No matter how hard he tried, Ahmed couldn't _____ the pump to working order.

8. The children all gathered to _____ the new pump in action.

Definitions

Write the spelling word that has the same, or almost the same, meaning.

9. a type of snake _____

10. fake; not real _____

11. busy; in use _____

12. to direct or rule a country or state
_____

13. the area where land meets water
_____

14. a person who has great skill in a particular area
_____

15. a reddish-brown metal
_____

16. to set something aside for later use _____

© Macmillan/McGraw-Hill

Name

Circle the misspelled words in the passage. Write the words correctly on the lines below.

It was a skorching day, and Fatima didn't feel like getting up. Just the simple moshun of sitting up seemed to be too much. The chief had decided to appoynt someone to teach the rest of the village how to use the new pump, and the people considered Fatima an expurt. Now she stood in front of them on the first day of the dry seesun. "Obsurve," she said as she gripped the handle.

1. _____   3. _____   5. _____

2. _____   4. _____   6. _____

Writing Activity

Write a paragraph about a time you learned to use something new. Use four words from your spelling list.

_____

_____

_____

_____

_____

_____

_____

_____

_____

_____

_____

_____

© Macmillan/McGraw-Hill

Name _____

Look at the words in each set below. One word in each set is spelled correctly. Use a pencil to fill in the circle next to the correct word. Before you begin, look at the sample set of words. Sample A has been done for you. Do Sample B by yourself. When you are sure you know what to do, you may go on with the rest of the page.

Sample A:

Ⓐ beyond
Ⓑ beeyond
Ⓒ beeond
Ⓓ beayond

Sample B:

Ⓔ loanly
Ⓕ lonely
Ⓖ loenly
Ⓗ lonly

1. Ⓐ python
   Ⓑ pithon
   Ⓒ piethon
   Ⓓ pytheon

2. Ⓔ skorching
   Ⓕ scorching
   Ⓖ scortching
   Ⓗ scoreching

3. Ⓐ seasen
   Ⓑ season
   Ⓒ seasin
   Ⓓ seasun

4. Ⓔ dozin
   Ⓕ dozzen
   Ⓖ duzzen
   Ⓗ dozen

5. Ⓐ motian
   Ⓑ motien
   Ⓒ motion
   Ⓓ motieon

6. Ⓔ phony
   Ⓕ phoney
   Ⓖ phonny
   Ⓗ phonney

7. Ⓐ acteve
   Ⓑ actuve
   Ⓒ acktive
   Ⓓ active

8. Ⓔ cannvas
   Ⓕ canvas
   Ⓖ canves
   Ⓗ canvis

9. Ⓐ expirt
   Ⓑ exspert
   Ⓒ expert
   Ⓓ expurt

10. Ⓔ embrace
    Ⓕ embrase
    Ⓖ embraice
    Ⓗ embraise

11. Ⓐ coastel
    Ⓑ coastal
    Ⓒ coastul
    Ⓓ coastol

12. Ⓔ risserve
    Ⓕ riserve
    Ⓖ resserve
    Ⓗ reserve

13. Ⓐ govern
    Ⓑ guvern
    Ⓒ govvern
    Ⓓ govurn

14. Ⓔ flury
    Ⓕ flurry
    Ⓖ flurrey
    Ⓗ flurree

15. Ⓐ kopper
    Ⓑ coper
    Ⓒ copper
    Ⓓ copperr

16. Ⓔ appoint
    Ⓕ apoint
    Ⓖ appoinnt
    Ⓗ eppoint

17. Ⓐ baside
    Ⓑ beeside
    Ⓒ besside
    Ⓓ beside

18. Ⓔ cacoon
    Ⓕ cocoon
    Ⓖ coccoon
    Ⓗ caccoon

19. Ⓐ restore
    Ⓑ ristore
    Ⓒ restoer
    Ⓓ resstore

20. Ⓔ obsserve
    Ⓕ abserve
    Ⓖ observe
    Ⓗ obbserve

© Macmillan/McGraw-Hill

Name_____

Fold back the paper along the dotted line. Write the words in the blanks as they are read aloud. When you finish the test, unfold the paper. Use the list at the right to correct any spelling mistakes.

1. _____
2. _____
3. _____
4. _____
5. _____
6. _____
7. _____
8. _____
9. _____
10. _____
11. _____
12. _____
13. _____
14. _____
15. _____
16. _____
17. _____
18. _____
19. _____
20. _____

Review Words 21. _____

22. _____

23. _____

Challenge Words 24. _____

25. _____

1. sugar
2. gentler
3. scissors
4. founder
5. director
6. scholar
7. saucer
8. labor
9. commander
10. error
11. crater
12. pillar
13. splendor
14. peddler
15. professor
16. shatter
17. governor
18. vapor
19. equator
20. soldier
21. appoint
22. season
23. canvas
24. refrigerator
25. remainder

© Macmillan/McGraw-Hill

At Home: Help the student practice the words he or she missed to prepare for the Posttest.

Name_____

Using the Word Study Steps

1. LOOK at the word.

2. SAY the word aloud.

3. STUDY the letters in the word.

4. WRITE the word.

5. CHECK the word.
Did you spell the word right?
If not, go back to step 1.

Find and Circle

Find and circle each of the spelling words in this puzzle. Words may read forward, backward, upward, downward, or diagonally.

```
R  R  E  T  A  R  C  I  P  R  O  F  E  S  S  O  R  S
C  E  E  R  R  O  R  N  B  J  K  H  X  S  G  R  R  R
K  R  D  T  T  N  W  J  V  O  I  M  M  Y  M  O  E  R
O  O  G  N  R  O  D  N  E  L  P  S  S  Z  S  I  V  A
E  B  O  R  A  D  I  R  E  C  T  O  R  S  D  A  R  L
Q  A  V  W  E  M  R  A  G  U  S  J  I  L  P  O  E  O
U  L  E  C  Q  D  M  H  J  C  O  C  O  O  X  O  C  H
A  W  R  R  U  Q  N  O  W  F  S  S  R  R  D  A  U  C
T  T  N  K  Z  X  X  U  C  S  H  A  T  T  E  R  A  S
O  M  O  D  P  S  S  Z  O  G  E  N  T  L  E  R  S  R
R  A  R  P  I  L  L  A  R  F  O  P  E  D  D  L  E  R
```

List the words below as you find them in the puzzle.

1. _____   11. _____

2. _____   12. _____

3. _____   13. _____

4. _____   14. _____

5. _____   15. _____

6. _____   16. _____

7. _____   17. _____

8. _____   18. _____

9. _____   19. _____

10. _____   20. _____

At Home: Review the Word Study Steps above to help the student spell new words.

© Macmillan/McGraw-Hill

Name_____

commander	vapor	professor	founder
gentler	shatter	governor	crater
labor	peddler	splendor	director
error	pillar	sugar	saucer
soldier	scissors	equator	scholar

Sort each spelling word by finding the sound and spelling pattern to which it belongs. Write the spelling words with the /schwa-r/ spelled:

-or

1. _____   6. _____

2. _____   7. _____

3. _____   8. _____

4. _____   9. _____

5. _____

-er

1. _____   5. _____

2. _____   6. _____

3. _____   7. _____

4. _____   8. _____

-ar

1. _____

2. _____

3. _____

© Macmillan/McGraw-Hill

Name_____

commander	vapor	professor	founder
gentler	shatter	governor	crater
labor	peddler	splendor	director
error	pillar	sugar	saucer
soldier	scissors	equator	scholar

What's the Word?

Complete each sentence with a spelling word.

1. Danny used _____ to cut a hole in the board.

2. The powdery substance on the floor looked like _____.

3. The meteor made a huge _____ in the ground outside the house.

4. Danny thought that he had made an _____ in the game.

5. Walter hoped that the meteor wouldn't _____ the television.

6. The ship's _____ pointed a laser at the Budwing house.

7. Danny often wished that Walter would be _____ when he teased him.

8. A flying _____ hovered several feet from the window.

9. With his helmet and boots, the robot looked a little like a _____.

10. The spaceship knocked out a _____ that supported the living room ceiling.

Meaning Match

Write the spelling word that matches each clue below.

11. line around the middle of Earth _____

12. gas _____

13. hard work _____

14. person in charge of a project _____

15. advanced student _____

16. traveling salesperson _____

© Macmillan/McGraw-Hill

Name_____

Circle the misspelled words in the passage. Write the words correctly on the lines below.

Danny and Walter were sitting inside when the entire house began to shake. It felt as if the windows could shattur at any moment. Slowly, a mysterious vapur started pouring in from underneath the door. Walter almost dropped the scissers he was holding as the flying sauser knocked over a piller just outside the house. When they looked outside, there was a huge krater in the driveway.

1. _____ 3. _____ 5. _____

2. _____ 4. _____ 6. _____

Writing Activity

Write a paragraph about a game that you like to play. Use four spelling words in your paragraph.

_____
_____
_____
_____
_____
_____
_____
_____
_____
_____
_____
_____
_____
_____

© Macmillan/McGraw-Hill

Name _____

Look at the words in each set below. One word in each set is spelled correctly. Use a pencil to fill in the circle next to the correct word. Before you begin, look at the sample set of words. Sample A has been done for you. Do Sample B by yourself. When you are sure you know what to do, you may go on with the rest of the page.

Sample A:

Ⓐ begar
Ⓑ beggar
Ⓒ beggarr
Ⓓ baggar

Sample B:

Ⓔ actor
Ⓕ acktor
Ⓖ acter
Ⓗ actar

1. Ⓐ directer
   Ⓑ director
   Ⓒ directar
   Ⓓ direcktor

2. Ⓔ shater
   Ⓕ shatter
   Ⓖ shattar
   Ⓗ shattur

3. Ⓐ soldier
   Ⓑ soldiur
   Ⓒ soldiar
   Ⓓ soldierr

4. Ⓔ govenor
   Ⓕ governer
   Ⓖ governor
   Ⓗ govener

5. Ⓐ errar
   Ⓑ error
   Ⓒ eror
   Ⓓ errarr

6. Ⓔ commandder
   Ⓕ commannder
   Ⓖ comander
   Ⓗ commander

7. Ⓐ peddlor
   Ⓑ peddlar
   Ⓒ peddler
   Ⓓ pedler

8. Ⓔ professor
   Ⓕ professer
   Ⓖ professur
   Ⓗ professar

9. Ⓐ piller
   Ⓑ pilar
   Ⓒ pillar
   Ⓓ pillur

10. Ⓔ splender
    Ⓕ splendor
    Ⓖ splendar
    Ⓗ splendur

11. Ⓐ sissors
    Ⓑ scissors
    Ⓒ scissers
    Ⓓ scissurs

12. Ⓔ vapper
    Ⓕ vappor
    Ⓖ vaper
    Ⓗ vapor

13. Ⓐ scolar
    Ⓑ scholar
    Ⓒ scholer
    Ⓓ scholor

14. Ⓔ sugar
    Ⓕ sugor
    Ⓖ suger
    Ⓗ suggar

15. Ⓐ equater
    Ⓑ equateor
    Ⓒ equator
    Ⓓ equatar

16. Ⓔ laber
    Ⓕ labar
    Ⓖ labeor
    Ⓗ labor

17. Ⓐ foundor
    Ⓑ foundar
    Ⓒ foundir
    Ⓓ founder

18. Ⓔ cratear
    Ⓕ crater
    Ⓖ cratar
    Ⓗ crator

19. Ⓐ saucer
    Ⓑ sauser
    Ⓒ sauceor
    Ⓓ saucear

20. Ⓔ gentlor
    Ⓕ gentlur
    Ⓖ gentlar
    Ⓗ gentler

© Macmillan/McGraw-Hill

Read each sentence. If an underlined word is spelled wrong, fill in the circle that goes with that word. If no word is spelled wrong, fill in the circle below NONE. Read Sample A and do Sample B.

NONE

A. Let's <u>appoint</u> an <u>expurt</u> this <u>season</u>.
        A   B   C

A. Ⓐ ⬤Ⓑ Ⓒ Ⓓ

NONE

B. The <u>scoler</u> and the <u>professor</u> discussed the <u>crater</u>.
        E   F   G

B. Ⓔ Ⓕ Ⓖ Ⓗ

NONE

1. The royal <u>governor</u> sent troops to <u>punnish</u> the <u>patriot</u>.
        A   B   C

1. Ⓐ Ⓑ Ⓒ Ⓓ

NONE

2. <u>Observe</u> the sled tracks to find their <u>reesent</u> <u>motion</u>.
     E   F   G

2. Ⓔ Ⓕ Ⓖ Ⓗ

NONE

3. This <u>season</u>, you can <u>obsurve</u> <u>smoky</u> chimneys.
      A   B   C

3. Ⓐ Ⓑ Ⓒ Ⓓ

NONE

4. The <u>recent</u> snowfall was fun, <u>although</u> it made him <u>shivver</u>.
      E   F   G

4. Ⓔ Ⓕ Ⓖ Ⓗ

NONE

5. My mother is an <u>active</u> <u>scholar</u> and a <u>genuone</u> friend.
              A   B   C

5. Ⓐ Ⓑ Ⓒ Ⓓ

NONE

6. A <u>casual</u> sense of <u>humer</u> would <u>improve</u> my stories.
      E   F   G

6. Ⓔ Ⓕ Ⓖ Ⓗ

NONE

7. She used the new <u>sizzers</u> to <u>restore</u> the dress' <u>splendor</u>.
             A   B   C

7. Ⓐ Ⓑ Ⓒ Ⓓ

NONE

8. Her <u>genuine</u> story convinced the <u>casuel</u> crowd in an <u>instant</u>.
      E   F   G

8. Ⓔ Ⓕ Ⓖ Ⓗ

NONE

9. I could <u>emprove</u> on the <u>piano</u> if my fingers did not <u>meander</u>.
        A   B   C

9. Ⓐ Ⓑ Ⓒ Ⓓ

NONE

10. If you don't <u>panic</u>, you won't <u>shatter</u> the bottle of <u>fewal</u>.
       E   F   G

10. Ⓔ Ⓕ Ⓖ Ⓗ

NONE

11. The damp <u>fuel</u> made the fire <u>smokie</u>, not <u>scorching</u>.
      A   B   C

11. Ⓐ Ⓑ Ⓒ Ⓓ

© Macmillan/McGraw-Hill

12. The skorching sun could ruin the canvas tent by
      E   F   G

    causing its color to fade.

NONE

12. Ⓔ Ⓕ Ⓖ Ⓗ

13. A reckless error could rooen everything.
     A   B   C

NONE

13. Ⓐ Ⓑ Ⓒ Ⓓ

14. When will the city restoar the local fairground?
              E   F   G

NONE

14. Ⓔ Ⓕ Ⓖ Ⓗ

15. The landlord found an errer in the address book.
     A   B   C

NONE

15. Ⓐ Ⓑ Ⓒ Ⓓ

16. Don't meandor, stay near your partner, and try not to panic.
      E   F   G

NONE

16. Ⓔ Ⓕ Ⓖ Ⓗ

17. Her tennis parttner was an instant expert at the game.
          A   B C

NONE

17. Ⓐ Ⓑ Ⓒ Ⓓ

18. He waved the scissors in a recklace motion.
           E   F   G

NONE

18. Ⓔ Ⓕ Ⓖ Ⓗ

19. The music's splender made us shiver for an instant.
        A   B   C

NONE

19. Ⓐ Ⓑ Ⓒ Ⓓ

20. The lawyer had no sense of humor and made a
                    E

    moshun to punish the man.
      F   G

NONE

20. Ⓔ Ⓕ Ⓖ Ⓗ

21. The schollar was an expert witness at the trial.
      A   B   C

NONE

21. Ⓐ Ⓑ Ⓒ Ⓓ

22. The landlord lost her local adress book.
      E   F   G

NONE

22. Ⓔ Ⓕ Ⓖ Ⓗ

23. The smoky fire is scorching the enstant potatoes.
     A   B   C

NONE

23. Ⓐ Ⓑ Ⓒ Ⓓ

24. Just one error could shadder and ruin the glass.
        E   F   G

NONE

24. Ⓔ Ⓕ Ⓖ Ⓗ

25. He is in constant motion, always doing aktive labor
              A   B   C

    in the garden.

NONE

25. Ⓐ Ⓑ Ⓒ Ⓓ

© Macmillan/McGraw-Hill

Name_____

Fold back the paper along the dotted line. Write the words in the blanks as they are read aloud. When you finish the test, unfold the paper. Use the list at the right to correct any spelling mistakes.

1. _____
2. _____
3. _____
4. _____
5. _____
6. _____
7. _____
8. _____
9. _____
10. _____
11. _____
12. _____
13. _____
14. _____
15. _____
16. _____
17. _____
18. _____
19. _____
20. _____

Review Words 21. _____
22. _____
23. _____
Challenge Words 24. _____
25. _____

1. slogan
2. woolen
3. listen
4. heron
5. frighten
6. lengthen
7. captain
8. mountain
9. sandal
10. signal
11. global
12. bushel
13. marvel
14. barrel
15. practical
16. pretzel
17. fable
18. chuckle
19. angle
20. nozzle
21. scissors
22. pillar
23. governor
24. dungeon
25. salmon

At Home: Help the student practice the words he or she missed to prepare for the Posttest.

Goin' Someplace Special
Grade 5/Unit 4
97

© Macmillan/McGraw-Hill

Spelling

Words with /schwa-l/
and /schwa-n/:
Practice

Name_____

Using the Word Study Steps

1. LOOK at the word.

2. SAY the word aloud.

3. STUDY the letters in the word.

4. WRITE the word.

5. CHECK the word.
   Did you spell the word right?
   If not, go back to step 1.

Fill-Ins

Fill in the missing letters of each word to form a spelling word.

1. ang ___ ___

2. her ___ ___

3. length ___ ___

4. marv ___ ___

5. wool ___ ___

6. list ___ ___

7. bush ___ ___

8. sign ___ ___

9. nozz ___ ___

10. practic ___ ___

11. barr ___ ___

12. capt ___ ___ ___

13. fright ___ ___

14. slog ___ ___

15. mount ___ ___ ___

16. pretz ___ ___

17. fab ___ ___

18. glob ___ ___

19. sand ___ ___

20. chuck ___ ___

Alphabetical Order

Use the lines below to write the spelling words in alphabetical order.

1. _____

2. _____

3. _____

4. _____

5. _____

6. _____

7. _____

8. _____

9. _____

10. _____

11. _____

12. _____

13. _____

14. _____

15. _____

16. _____

17. _____

18. _____

19. _____

20. _____

At Home: Review the Word Study Steps above to help the
student spell new words.

© Macmillan/McGraw-Hill

Name_____

practical	lengthen	bushel	pretzel
marvel	barrel	nozzle	slogan
chuckle	global	woolen	frighten
sandal	signal	fable	captain
heron	listen	mountain	angle

Sort each spelling word by finding the sound and spelling pattern to which it belongs. Write the spelling words with the /schwa-l/ spelled:

-el

1. _____
2. _____
3. _____
4. _____

-al

1. _____
2. _____
3. _____
4. _____

-le

1. _____
2. _____
3. _____
4. _____

Write the spelling words with the /schwa-n/ spelled:

-on

1. _____

-an

1. _____

-en

1. _____
2. _____
3. _____
4. _____

-ain

1. _____
2. _____

© Macmillan/McGraw-Hill

Name_____

Spelling

Words with /schwa-l/
and /schwa-n/:
Word Meaning

practical	lengthen	bushel	pretzel
marvel	barrel	nozzle	slogan
chuckle	global	woolen	frighten
sandal	signal	fable	captain
heron	listen	mountain	angle

Fill in the Blanks

Complete each sentence with a spelling word.

1. 'Tricia Ann ate her _____ on a bench marked *Whites Only*.

2. The _____ made an announcement over the loudspeaker.

3. When 'Tricia Ann reached the library, there was mud on her left

   _____.

4. The traffic _____ turned red as she crossed the street.

5. The _____ of cherries cost four dollars at the market.

6. A thin, white _____ flew across the sky.

7. She knew it was late by looking at the _____ of the sun.

8. The shoemaker tried to _____ 'Tricia Ann's boot by half an inch.

9. The man adjusted the _____ on the hose to rinse off the library steps.

10. The Mission Church had _____ blankets to keep people warm in the winter.

Synonyms

Write the spelling word that comes closest in meaning to each word below.

11. worldwide _____   15. useful _____

12. motto _____   16. scare _____

13. story _____   17. container _____

14. laugh _____   18. wonder _____

© Macmillan/McGraw-Hill

Spelling

Words with /schwa-l/
and /schwa-n/:
Proofreading

Name_____

Circle the misspelled words in the passage. Write the words correctly on the lines below.

'Tricia Ann was having trouble finding her left sandel. The mountan hike started at three o'clock, and she was running late. She tried to think back to the last time she wore the shoes. "I put them in a practicul place where I wouldn't lose them," she said aloud. All of a sudden, she let out a chuckel. The lost shoe was underneath the wullen blanket by her bed! Tying the last of the straps, she grabbed a pretsel and ran out the door.

1. _____   3. _____   5. _____

2. _____   4. _____   6. _____

Writing Activity

Write a paragraph about a person you know or have read about who was treated unfairly. Use four words from your spelling list.

_____

_____

_____

_____

_____

_____

_____

_____

_____

© Macmillan/McGraw-Hill

Spelling

Words with /schwa-l/
and /schwa-n/:
Posttest

Name_____

Look at the words in each set below. One word in each set is spelled correctly. Use a pencil to fill in the circle next to the correct word. Before you begin, look at the sample set of words. Sample A has been done for you. Do Sample B by yourself. When you are sure you know what to do, you may go on with the rest of the page.

Sample A:

- Ⓐ bottel
- Ⓑ botle
- Ⓒ bottle
- Ⓓ bottul

Sample B:

- Ⓔ sharpin
- Ⓕ sharpun
- Ⓖ sharppen
- Ⓗ sharpen

1.
- Ⓐ angul
- Ⓑ angle
- Ⓒ angal
- Ⓓ angull

2.
- Ⓔ herron
- Ⓕ heron
- Ⓖ herun
- Ⓗ herrun

3.
- Ⓐ langthen
- Ⓑ lengthun
- Ⓒ lengthin
- Ⓓ lengthen

4.
- Ⓔ marvell
- Ⓕ marvul
- Ⓖ marvel
- Ⓗ marval

5.
- Ⓐ woolen
- Ⓑ woollen
- Ⓒ woolun
- Ⓓ woollun

6.
- Ⓔ listin
- Ⓕ listun
- Ⓖ lissen
- Ⓗ listen

7.
- Ⓐ bushel
- Ⓑ bushshel
- Ⓒ bushul
- Ⓓ bushell

8.
- Ⓔ signal
- Ⓕ signul
- Ⓖ signall
- Ⓗ cignal

9.
- Ⓐ nozzal
- Ⓑ nozzel
- Ⓒ nozzle
- Ⓓ nossle

10.
- Ⓔ practicul
- Ⓕ practical
- Ⓖ practicall
- Ⓗ practicel

11.
- Ⓐ barrel
- Ⓑ barel
- Ⓒ barrell
- Ⓓ barral

12.
- Ⓔ capten
- Ⓕ captain
- Ⓖ captin
- Ⓗ captun

13.
- Ⓐ frightun
- Ⓑ friten
- Ⓒ frighten
- Ⓓ frightin

14.
- Ⓔ slogan
- Ⓕ slogean
- Ⓖ slowgan
- Ⓗ slogen

15.
- Ⓐ mounten
- Ⓑ mountain
- Ⓒ mowntain
- Ⓓ mountan

16.
- Ⓔ pretsel
- Ⓕ pretzul
- Ⓖ pretzle
- Ⓗ pretzel

17.
- Ⓐ fable
- Ⓑ fabel
- Ⓒ fabull
- Ⓓ fabill

18.
- Ⓔ globul
- Ⓕ globel
- Ⓖ globle
- Ⓗ global

19.
- Ⓐ sandal
- Ⓑ sandle
- Ⓒ sandel
- Ⓓ sandul

20.
- Ⓔ chuckel
- Ⓕ chuckle
- Ⓖ chuckil
- Ⓗ chuckul

© Macmillan/McGraw-Hill

Name _____

Fold back the paper along the dotted line. Write the words in the blanks as they are read aloud. When you finish the test, unfold the paper. Use the list at the right to correct any spelling mistakes.

1. _____
2. _____
3. _____
4. _____
5. _____
6. _____
7. _____
8. _____
9. _____
10. _____
11. _____
12. _____
13. _____
14. _____
15. _____
16. _____
17. _____
18. _____
19. _____
20. _____

Review Words 21. _____
22. _____
23. _____
Challenge Words 24. _____
25. _____

1. grownup
2. power
3. shower
4. bestow
5. August
6. allow
7. encounter
8. grouchy
9. rowdy
10. laundry
11. flawless
12. coward
13. lawyer
14. applause
15. arousing
16. faucet
17. trousers
18. caution
19. boundary
20. doubting
21. angle
22. mountain
23. sandal
24. southern
25. roughness

© Macmillan/McGraw-Hill

At Home: Help the student practice the words he or she missed to prepare for the Posttest.

Carlos and the Skunk
Grade 5/Unit 4

103

Name_____

Using the Word Study Steps

1. LOOK at the word.

2. SAY the word aloud.

3. STUDY the letters in the word.

4. WRITE the word.

5. CHECK the word.
   Did you spell the word right?
   If not, go back to step 1.

Find and Circle

Find and circle each of the spelling words in this puzzle. Words may read forward, backward, upward, or downward.

```
R E Y W A L E I G Y W O L L A J C T A F
S H O W E R B F R R W O T S E B O N R L
A P P L A U S E O A Y H C U O R G I O A
D R A W O C S N W D R E W O P N V Z U W
C A U T I O N R N N T R O U S E R S S L
D O U B T I N G U U T S U G U A P N I E
F A U C E T L U P O L A U N D R Y A N S
R E T N U O C N E B R O W D Y D J A G S
```

List the words below as you find them in the puzzle.

1. _____   6. _____   11. _____   16. _____

2. _____   7. _____   12. _____   17. _____

3. _____   8. _____   13. _____   18. _____

4. _____   9. _____   14. _____   19. _____

5. _____   10. _____   15. _____   20. _____

At Home: Review the Word Study Steps above to help the student spell new words.

© Macmillan/McGraw-Hill

Name _____

encounter	August	faucet	shower
lawyer	rowdy	trousers	doubting
power	grouchy	applause	boundary
allow	bestow	coward	grownup
flawless	caution	laundry	arousing

Determine which syllable is stressed in each of the spelling words. Then sort the words into the correct columns below.

First syllable is stressed

1. _____ 9. _____

2. _____ 10. _____

3. _____ 11. _____

4. _____ 12. _____

5. _____ 13. _____

6. _____ 14. _____

7. _____ 15. _____

8. _____

Second syllable is stressed

1. _____

2. _____

3. _____

4. _____

5. _____

© Macmillan/McGraw-Hill

Name _____

encounter	August	faucet	shower
lawyer	rowdy	trousers	doubting
power	grouchy	applause	boundary
allow	bestow	coward	grownup
flawless	caution	laundry	arousing

Replacements

Write the spelling word that can replace the boldfaced word or words in each sentence.

1. Carlos' skunk-trapping idea was nearly **perfect**. _____

2. Five minutes of **clapping** followed the concert. _____

3. I don't know why he was **in a bad mood** yesterday. _____

4. Do you think Gloria will **permit** me to see her again? _____

5. She held a cup under the kitchen **tap** to get some water.

   _____

6. The skunk walked along the **border** of their property. _____

7. Carlos, there's a huge pile of **dirty clothes** in the corner! _____

8. I always use **care** when going near wild animals. _____

9. Carlos had trouble getting the smell out of his **pants**. _____

10. Why is he acting like such a **scared person**? _____

It Takes Three

Write a spelling word that goes with the other two words.

11. adult, parent _____

12. soap, bath _____

13. teacher, doctor _____

14. September, December _____

15. give, donate _____

© Macmillan/McGraw-Hill

Name_____

Circle the misspelled words in the passage. Write the words correctly on the lines below.

Carlos was in a growchy mood. He had been washing his hands under the fawcet for five minutes, trying to make the smell go away. At this rate, he would have to take yet another shouer. How was he supposed to know that he would incounter a skunk? Now he knew why his mother didn't alow him to wander around outside alone. Next time, he would use more caushion around animals.

1. _____   3. _____   5. _____

2. _____   4. _____   6. _____

Writing Activity

Write a paragraph about a time when you encountered an animal. Use four words from your spelling list.

_____

_____

_____

_____

_____

_____

_____

_____

_____

_____

_____

_____

_____

© Macmillan/McGraw-Hill

Name _____

Look at the words in each set below. One word in each set is spelled correctly. Use a pencil to fill in the circle next to the correct word. Before you begin, look at the sample set of words. Sample A has been done for you. Do Sample B by yourself. When you are sure you know what to do, you may go on with the rest of the page.

Sample A:
- (A) fountain
- (B) fowntain
- (C) founten
- (D) fountin

Sample B:
- (E) powdder
- (F) pouder
- (G) powder
- (H) powderr

1.
- (A) allow
- (B) ellow
- (C) alow
- (D) allou

2.
- (E) arrousing
- (F) arousing
- (G) aroussing
- (H) arowsing

3.
- (A) boundary
- (B) boundry
- (C) boundery
- (D) bowndary

4.
- (E) beestow
- (F) bistow
- (G) bestow
- (H) bestowe

5.
- (A) grounup
- (B) grownup
- (C) grownnup
- (D) grownupp

6.
- (E) coword
- (F) cowerd
- (G) cowward
- (H) coward

7.
- (A) doubting
- (B) doubtting
- (C) douting
- (D) dowting

8.
- (E) rowddy
- (F) rowdy
- (G) rowdie
- (H) roudy

9.
- (A) encownter
- (B) encountter
- (C) incounter
- (D) encounter

10.
- (E) powwer
- (F) power
- (G) powerr
- (H) powwerr

11.
- (A) shower
- (B) showwer
- (C) showerr
- (D) showwerr

12.
- (E) trouzers
- (F) trowsers
- (G) trousers
- (H) trousures

13.
- (A) growchy
- (B) grouchy
- (C) grouchee
- (D) grouchie

14.
- (E) applause
- (F) upplause
- (G) uplause
- (H) aplause

15.
- (A) loiyer
- (B) lawer
- (C) loyer
- (D) lawyer

16.
- (E) Auggust
- (F) Awgust
- (G) August
- (H) Augusst

17.
- (A) laundry
- (B) lawndry
- (C) laundree
- (D) laundrie

18.
- (E) caution
- (F) caushion
- (G) cawtion
- (H) cawshun

19.
- (A) flawlless
- (B) flawless
- (C) flawles
- (D) flawliss

20.
- (E) faucit
- (F) fawcet
- (G) faucet
- (H) fauset

© Macmillan/McGraw-Hill

Name_____

Fold back the paper along the dotted line. Write the words in the blanks as they are read aloud. When you finish the test, unfold the paper. Use the list at the right to correct any spelling mistakes.

1. _____
2. _____
3. _____
4. _____
5. _____
6. _____
7. _____
8. _____
9. _____
10. _____
11. _____
12. _____
13. _____
14. _____
15. _____
16. _____
17. _____
18. _____
19. _____
20. _____

Review Words 21. _____
22. _____
23. _____

Challenge Words 24. _____
25. _____

1. contest
2. content
3. protest
4. combat
5. permits
6. rebel
7. present
8. insert
9. desert
10. subject
11. minute
12. compact
13. conduct
14. contract
15. refuse
16. conflict
17. research
18. record
19. entrance
20. extract
21. doubting
22. allow
23. caution
24. effect
25. affect

© Macmillan/McGraw-Hill

At Home: Help the student practice the words he or she missed to prepare for the Posttest.

Name_____

Using the Word Study Steps

1. LOOK at the word.

2. SAY the word aloud.

3. STUDY the letters in the word.

4. WRITE the word.

5. CHECK the word.
   Did you spell the word right?
   If not, go back to step 1.

Find and Circle

Find and circle each of the spelling words in this puzzle. Words may read forward, backward, upward, downward, or diagonally.

```
C E S U F E R F T T T E M T K E T T E T Y H
O C O M B A T G N S C M F G E R C N C C C S
N M I N U T E D E E U H I K E I T A O R I U
T Y P G N Q A N T T D G V S L R R M A J C B
R T S E T N O C N O N B E F A T P E X X H J
A T R E S N I F O R O D N N X A S V K I W E
C P R E S E N T C P C O C E C E L E B E R C
T P E R M I T S W N C E L T R R E C O R D T
```

List the words below as you find them in the puzzle.

1. _____   6. _____   11. _____   16. _____

2. _____   7. _____   12. _____   17. _____

3. _____   8. _____   13. _____   18. _____

4. _____   9. _____   14. _____   19. _____

5. _____   10. _____   15. _____   20. _____

At Home: Review the Word Study Steps above to help the student spell new words.

© Macmillan/McGraw-Hill

Name _____

refuse	contest	entrance	present
insert	permits	minute	extract
desert	rebel	contract	compact
subject	conduct	research	conflict
combat	record	protest	content

Write the spelling words in alphabetical order.

1. _____   11. _____

2. _____   12. _____

3. _____   13. _____

4. _____   14. _____

5. _____   15. _____

6. _____   16. _____

7. _____   17. _____

8. _____   18. _____

9. _____   19. _____

10. _____   20. _____

Make a Puzzle

Make up a puzzle of your own using the space on this page. Give it to someone else to solve. Be sure to include at least five spelling words in your puzzle.

© Macmillan/McGraw-Hill

Name_____

refuse	contest	entrance	present
insert	permits	minute	extract
desert	rebel	contract	compact
subject	conduct	research	conflict
combat	record	protest	content

Where's the accent?

For each of the spelling words above, the meaning varies according to where the accent is placed. Circle the choice that best completes each sentence. The accented syllable is shown in bold.

1. There was a huge _____ between the two candidates. (**con**flict, con**flict**)

2. A special team was assigned to _____ the voter data. (**re**search, re**search**)

3. The president held a meeting to _____ his findings. (**pre**sent, pre**sent**)

4. Voting only takes one _____ of your time. (**min**ute, mi**nute**)

5. The reporter tried to _____ an interview. (**con**duct, con**duct**)

6. You may _____ to admit how you voted. (**re**fuse, re**fuse**)

7. The Democrats wanted to _____ the results. (**con**test, con**test**)

8. The government _____ every citizen to vote. (**per**mits, per**mits**)

9. The Republican President spoke on the _____ of war. (**sub**ject, sub**ject**)

10. The _____ of the President's speech was interesting. (**con**tent, con**tent**)

© Macmillan/McGraw-Hill

Name_____

Circle the misspelled words in the passage. Write the words correctly on the lines below.

A small crowd gathered outside the White House to hear the President speak. The subjeckt of his speech was voting. A team of experts had done resurch about how many people actually voted. "There is no eksuse for not voting," he began. "The Constitution purmits each of you to take part in the election process. I intend to conduckt a survey asking people why they chose not to vote. When I have that information, I will preesent it to you so that we may work on solving this problem."

1. _____   3. _____   5. _____

2. _____   4. _____   6. _____

Writing Activity

Write a paragraph about what you could do to encourage more people to vote in presidential elections. Use four words from your spelling list.

_____

_____

_____

_____

_____

_____

_____

_____

_____

_____

_____

© Macmillan/McGraw-Hill

Name_____

Look at the words in each set below. One word in each set is
spelled correctly. Use a pencil to fill in the circle next to the correct
word. Before you begin, look at the sample set of words. Sample
A has been done for you. Do Sample B by yourself. When you are
sure you know what to do, you may go on with the rest of the page.

Sample A:

Ⓐ effect
Ⓑ efect
Ⓒ iffect
Ⓓ effekt

Sample B:

Ⓔ afect
Ⓕ affect
Ⓖ afekt
Ⓗ uffect

1. Ⓐ excuse
   Ⓑ excusse
   Ⓒ exxcuse
   Ⓓ escuse

2. Ⓔ conttest
   Ⓕ contest
   Ⓖ conntest
   Ⓗ connttest

3. Ⓐ conntent
   Ⓑ content
   Ⓒ conttent
   Ⓓ connttent

4. Ⓔ refuze
   Ⓕ reffuse
   Ⓖ rifuse
   Ⓗ refuse

5. Ⓐ proetest
   Ⓑ prottest
   Ⓒ protest
   Ⓓ protestt

6. Ⓔ conduckt
   Ⓕ condduct
   Ⓖ conduct
   Ⓗ connduct

7. Ⓐ subject
   Ⓑ subgect
   Ⓒ subbject
   Ⓓ subjeckt

8. Ⓔ extract
   Ⓕ exttract
   Ⓖ exstract
   Ⓗ extrackt

9. Ⓐ permmits
   Ⓑ permits
   Ⓒ permitts
   Ⓓ purmits

10. Ⓔ inssert
    Ⓕ incert
    Ⓖ insert
    Ⓗ insertt

11. Ⓐ desert
    Ⓑ desurt
    Ⓒ dessurt
    Ⓓ dezert

12. Ⓔ reble
    Ⓕ rebbel
    Ⓖ rebel
    Ⓗ rebble

13. Ⓐ combat
    Ⓑ combbat
    Ⓒ combatt
    Ⓓ commbat

14. Ⓔ confflict
    Ⓕ conflickt
    Ⓖ connflict
    Ⓗ conflict

15. Ⓐ risearch
    Ⓑ research
    Ⓒ ressearch
    Ⓓ resurch

16. Ⓔ compact
    Ⓕ commpact
    Ⓖ comppact
    Ⓗ compactt

17. Ⓐ conttract
    Ⓑ contractt
    Ⓒ contract
    Ⓓ conntract

18. Ⓔ enttrance
    Ⓕ entrence
    Ⓖ entrunce
    Ⓗ entrance

19. Ⓐ present
    Ⓑ prezent
    Ⓒ pressent
    Ⓓ presunt

20. Ⓔ minnute
    Ⓕ minute
    Ⓖ minnut
    Ⓗ minuht

© Macmillan/McGraw-Hill

Name_____

Fold back the paper along the dotted line. Write the words in the blanks as they are read aloud. When you finish the test, unfold the paper. Use the list at the right to correct any spelling mistakes.

1. _____
2. _____
3. _____
4. _____
5. _____
6. _____
7. _____
8. _____
9. _____
10. _____
11. _____
12. _____
13. _____
14. _____
15. _____
16. _____
17. _____
18. _____
19. _____
20. _____

Review Words 21. _____
22. _____
23. _____

Challenge Words 24. _____
25. _____

1. rancher
2. searcher
3. enclosure
4. future
5. butcher
6. measure
7. pleasure
8. mixture
9. treasure
10. feature
11. pasture
12. creature
13. lecture
14. gesture
15. nature
16. fracture
17. moisture
18. stretcher
19. legislature
20. azure
21. contest
22. desert
23. entrance
24. miniature
25. disclosure

© Macmillan/McGraw-Hill

 At Home: Help the student practice the words he or she missed to prepare for the Posttest.

Name_____

Using the Word Study Steps

1. LOOK at the word.

2. SAY the word aloud.

3. STUDY the letters in the word.

4. WRITE the word.

5. CHECK the word.
   Did you spell the word right?
   If not, go back to step 1.

Fill-Ins

Fill in the missing letters of each word to form a spelling word.

1. fu ___ ___ ___ e

2. crea ___ ___ ___ e

3. sear ___ ___ ___ ___

4. fea ___ ___ ___ e

5. frac ___ ___ ___ e

6. ges ___ ___ ___ e

7. legisla ___ ___ ___ e

8. enclo ___ ___ ___ e

9. mea ___ ___ ___ e

10. mix ___ ___ ___ e

11. mois ___ ___ ___ e

12. na ___ ___ ___ e

13. pas ___ ___ ___ e

14. plea ___ ___ ___ e

15. a ___ ___ ___ e

16. stret ___ ___ e ___

17. trea ___ ___ ___ e

18. ran ___ ___ e ___

19. but ___ ___ e ___

20. lec ___ ___ ___ e

Write the Words

Use the lines below to practice writing the spelling words.

1. _____   6. _____   11. _____   16. _____

2. _____   7. _____   12. _____   17. _____

3. _____   8. _____   13. _____   18. _____

4. _____   9. _____   14. _____   19. _____

5. _____   10. _____   15. _____   20. _____

© Macmillan/McGraw-Hill

At Home: Review the Word Study Steps above to help the student spell new words.

Name_____

stretcher	legislature	gesture	butcher
pasture	lecture	fracture	searcher
creature	rancher	nature	enclosure
feature	moisture	treasure	mixture
measure	azure	pleasure	future

Sort each spelling word by finding the sound and spelling pattern to which it belongs. Write the spelling words with the /ch[schwa]r/ spelled:

-ture

1. _____
2. _____
3. _____
4. _____
5. _____
6. _____
7. _____
8. _____
9. _____
10. _____
11. _____

-cher

1. _____
2. _____
3. _____
4. _____

Write the spelling words with the /zh[schwa]r/ spelled:

-sure

1. _____
2. _____
3. _____
4. _____

-zure

1. _____

© Macmillan/McGraw-Hill

Spelling
Words with
/ch[schwa]r/ and
/zh[schwa]r/:
Word Meaning

Name_____

stretcher	legislature	gesture	butcher
pasture	lecture	fracture	searcher
creature	rancher	nature	enclosure
feature	moisture	treasure	mixture
measure	azure	pleasure	future

Fill in the Blanks

Complete each sentence with a spelling word.

1. It's hard not to _____ when you're excited or nervous.

2. There was a small _____ in the tree branch after the hurricane hit.

3. It can feel hotter outside when there's more _____ in the air.

4. Scientists often try to _____ the humidity in the air.

5. There might be a hidden _____ somewhere on this island.

6. The students found shelter in a small _____.

7. The professor gave a _____ on the topic of weather.

8. The _____ shop was full of people getting food in preparation for the storm.

9. After the storm cleared, there was a beautiful _____ sky.

10. The storm brought a _____ of wind, rain, and flooding.

Definitions

Write the spelling word that has the same, or almost the same, meaning.

11. animal or living thing _____

12. person who looks for something _____

13. special attraction _____

14. law-making body _____

15. time after the present _____

© Macmillan/McGraw-Hill

Name

Spelling
Words with
/ch[schwa]r/ and
/zh[schwa]r/:
Proofreading

Circle the misspelled words in the passage. Write the words correctly on the lines below.

Andrew walked outside. He felt as if something were different. There wasn't a creechur in sight. There was more moysture in the air. The sky had changed from a beautiful asure to a dark gray. Soon there would be a mixchure of rain, wind, and flooding. Natchure was about to demonstrate the effects of a natural disaster. Andrew put a cup on the porch to meazure the rainfall and headed inside to watch.

1. _____   3. _____   5. _____

2. _____   4. _____   6. _____

Writing Activity

Write a paragraph about what you would do if you found out that a hurricane was going to hit your town. Use four words from your spelling list.

_____

_____

_____

_____

_____

_____

_____

_____

_____

_____

_____

© Macmillan/McGraw-Hill

Name_____

Look at the words in each set below. One word in each set is spelled correctly. Use a pencil to fill in the circle next to the correct word. Before you begin, look at the sample set of words. Sample A has been done for you. Do Sample B by yourself. When you are sure you know what to do, you may go on with the rest of the page.

Sample A:
- Ⓐ cullcher
- Ⓑ culcher
- Ⓒ cullture
- ⬤ culture

Sample B:
- Ⓔ teechur
- Ⓕ teachur
- Ⓖ teecher
- Ⓗ teacher

1.
- Ⓐ futur
- Ⓑ fewture
- Ⓒ fuchure
- Ⓓ future

2.
- Ⓔ creeture
- Ⓕ creature
- Ⓖ creture
- Ⓗ crieture

3.
- Ⓐ searchar
- Ⓑ sercher
- Ⓒ searcher
- Ⓓ searchur

4.
- Ⓔ feature
- Ⓕ feeture
- Ⓖ feture
- Ⓗ fieture

5.
- Ⓐ fracture
- Ⓑ frackture
- Ⓒ fracchure
- Ⓓ fractture

6.
- Ⓔ gestture
- Ⓕ gessture
- Ⓖ gesture
- Ⓗ gestur

7.
- Ⓐ legislaturre
- Ⓑ legislatture
- Ⓒ leggislature
- Ⓓ legislature

8.
- Ⓔ enklosure
- Ⓕ enclosure
- Ⓖ enclosher
- Ⓗ enkloshure

9.
- Ⓐ measure
- Ⓑ meazure
- Ⓒ mesure
- Ⓓ mezhure

10.
- Ⓔ mixcher
- Ⓕ micksture
- Ⓖ mixture
- Ⓗ mixtture

11.
- Ⓐ moistturre
- Ⓑ moisturre
- Ⓒ moistture
- Ⓓ moisture

12.
- Ⓔ naturre
- Ⓕ natture
- Ⓖ nachure
- Ⓗ nature

13.
- Ⓐ pasture
- Ⓑ passture
- Ⓒ pastture
- Ⓓ pasturre

14.
- Ⓔ plesure
- Ⓕ pleasure
- Ⓖ pleazure
- Ⓗ pleazhure

15.
- Ⓐ azurre
- Ⓑ azzure
- Ⓒ azure
- Ⓓ azzurre

16.
- Ⓔ stretcher
- Ⓕ stretchur
- Ⓖ stretchar
- Ⓗ stretchure

17.
- Ⓐ tresure
- Ⓑ treasure
- Ⓒ tressure
- Ⓓ trezzure

18.
- Ⓔ ranchir
- Ⓕ ranchur
- Ⓖ ranncher
- Ⓗ rancher

19.
- Ⓐ butcher
- Ⓑ bucher
- Ⓒ buttcher
- Ⓓ butcherr

20.
- Ⓔ leckture
- Ⓕ lecture
- Ⓖ lectture
- Ⓗ lectturre

© Macmillan/McGraw-Hill

Name _____

Fold back the paper along the dotted line. Write the words in the blanks as they are read aloud. When you finish the test, unfold the paper. Use the list at the right to correct any spelling mistakes.

1. _____
2. _____
3. _____
4. _____
5. _____
6. _____
7. _____
8. _____
9. _____
10. _____
11. _____
12. _____
13. _____
14. _____
15. _____
16. _____
17. _____
18. _____
19. _____
20. _____

Review Words 21. _____

22. _____

23. _____

Challenge Words 24. _____

25. _____

1. distance
2. importance
3. balance
4. attendance
5. absence
6. performance
7. dependence
8. substance
9. disturbance
10. appearance
11. assistance
12. ignorance
13. brilliance
14. ambulance
15. residence
16. radiance
17. resistance
18. reluctance
19. persistence
20. hesitance
21. creature
22. measure
23. rancher
24. vigilance
25. inference

© Macmillan/McGraw-Hill

At Home: Help the student practice the words he or she missed to prepare for the Posttest.

Catch of the Day! • **Grade 5/Unit 4** 121

Name_____

Using the Word Study Steps

1. LOOK at the word.

2. SAY the word aloud.

3. STUDY the letters in the word.

4. WRITE the word.

5. CHECK the word.
   Did you spell the word right?
   If not, go back to step 1.

Fill-Ins

Fill in the missing letters of each word to form a spelling word.

1. ignor ___ ___ ___ e

2. abs ___ ___ ___ e

3. persist ___ ___ ___ e

4. appea ___ ___ ___ ce

5. reluc ___ ___ ___ ce

6. resid ___ ___ ___ e

7. distur ___ ___ ___ ce

8. brill ___ ___ ce

9. ambu ___ ___ ___ ce

10. resis ___ ___ ___ ce

11. dista ___ ___ ___

12. assis ___ a ___ ___ e

13. ba ___ a ___ ___ e

14. rad ___ ___ n ___ e

15. impor ___ ___ n ___ e

16. hesit ___ ___ ___ e

17. depen ___ ___ ___ ce

18. subs ___ ___ n ___ e

19. atten ___ ___ ___ ce

20. perfor ___ ___ n ___ e

Use the spelling words above to help you write a poem of at least 4 lines.

21. _____

22. _____

23. _____

24. _____

At Home: Review the Word Study Steps above to help the student spell new words.

© Macmillan/McGraw-Hill

Name_____

ambulance	residence	assistance	reluctance
brilliance	dependence	persistence	disturbance
balance	hesitance	ignorance	importance
performance	substance	radiance	resistance
attendance	absence	appearance	distance

Sort each spelling word by finding the sound and spelling pattern to which it belongs. Write the spelling words that contain two syllables and are spelled:

-ence

1. _____

-ance

1. _____
2. _____
3. _____
4. _____

Write the spelling words that contain three syllables and are spelled:

-ence

1. _____
2. _____
3. _____

-ance

1. _____
2. _____
3. _____
4. _____
5. _____
6. _____
7. _____
8. _____
9. _____
10. _____
11. _____
12. _____

© Macmillan/McGraw-Hill

Name_____

ambulance	residence	assistance	reluctance
brilliance	dependence	persistence	disturbance
balance	hesitance	ignorance	importance
performance	substance	radiance	resistance
attendance	absence	appearance	distance

Definitions

Write the spelling word that has the same, or almost the same, meaning.

1. great intelligence; shininess _____

2. the need for someone or something _____

3. something that takes up space _____

4. the state of being against or opposed to doing something _____

5. the state of having little or no knowledge _____

6. the state of feeling unsure or having doubts _____

7. a glowing quality _____

8. opposition; a pull in the opposite direction _____

9. the act of being present _____

10. a public display or presentation _____

Fill in the Blanks

Complete each sentence with a spelling word.

11. The Fisher learned the _____ of being honest.

12. The Basketmaker was unable to keep her _____ on the log.

13. The _____ to the market was a little more than one mile.

14. After tricking the people carrying food, the Fisher returned to his

_____ .

15. After falling into the river, the Fisher was taken away in a(an)

_____ .

© Macmillan/McGraw-Hill

Name_____

Circle the misspelled words in the passage. Write the words correctly on the lines below.

The Basketmaker ran a distence of four miles to get to the village. Once she was there, she went straight to the residance of her friend, the Lumberjack. She told him of what the Fisher had done, and of the importence of teaching him a lesson. Finally, she asked for his assistince. The Lumberjack's appearence was stern at first, but he soon agreed to help. They would teach the Fisher their own lesson about balence!

1. _____   3. _____   5. _____

2. _____   4. _____   6. _____

Writing Activity

Write a paragraph about a time when you or someone you know played a trick on someone else. Use four words from your spelling list.

_____

_____

_____

_____

_____

_____

_____

_____

_____

_____

© Macmillan/McGraw-Hill

Name_____

Look at the words in each set below. One word in each set is spelled correctly. Use a pencil to fill in the circle next to the correct word. Before you begin, look at the sample set of words. Sample A has been done for you. Do Sample B by yourself. When you are sure you know what to do, you may go on with the rest of the page.

Sample A:
- Ⓐ inference
- Ⓑ infurance
- Ⓒ infrence
- Ⓓ infrince

Sample B:
- Ⓔ viggilance
- Ⓕ vigilance
- Ⓖ vigilence
- Ⓗ vigillence

1.
- Ⓐ ambullance
- Ⓑ ambbulance
- Ⓒ ambulence
- Ⓓ ambulance

2.
- Ⓔ apearance
- Ⓕ appearance
- Ⓖ appeerance
- Ⓗ appearence

3.
- Ⓐ assistance
- Ⓑ asistance
- Ⓒ assistence
- Ⓓ assisstance

4.
- Ⓔ attendance
- Ⓕ atendance
- Ⓖ attendence
- Ⓗ attenddance

5.
- Ⓐ brillience
- Ⓑ brilliance
- Ⓒ briliance
- Ⓓ brilience

6.
- Ⓔ deppendance
- Ⓕ deppendence
- Ⓖ dependance
- Ⓗ dependence

7.
- Ⓐ substence
- Ⓑ substance
- Ⓒ subbstance
- Ⓓ substtance

8.
- Ⓔ dissturbance
- Ⓕ disturbence
- Ⓖ disturbance
- Ⓗ dissturbence

9.
- Ⓐ balance
- Ⓑ ballance
- Ⓒ balence
- Ⓓ ballence

10.
- Ⓔ hesitance
- Ⓕ hesitence
- Ⓖ hesatance
- Ⓗ hesatence

11.
- Ⓐ ignorrance
- Ⓑ iggnorance
- Ⓒ ignorence
- Ⓓ ignorance

12.
- Ⓔ importtence
- Ⓕ importence
- Ⓖ importance
- Ⓗ importtance

13.
- Ⓐ performance
- Ⓑ performence
- Ⓒ performmance
- Ⓓ performmence

14.
- Ⓔ persistance
- Ⓕ persistence
- Ⓖ persisstance
- Ⓗ perssistance

15.
- Ⓐ raddiance
- Ⓑ radianse
- Ⓒ radience
- Ⓓ radiance

16.
- Ⓔ resistance
- Ⓕ resistence
- Ⓖ ressistance
- Ⓗ resisstance

17.
- Ⓐ relluctance
- Ⓑ reluctance
- Ⓒ reluctence
- Ⓓ relluctence

18.
- Ⓔ abscence
- Ⓕ abbsence
- Ⓖ absance
- Ⓗ absence

19.
- Ⓐ residence
- Ⓑ ressidence
- Ⓒ residance
- Ⓓ ressidance

20.
- Ⓔ disstance
- Ⓕ distence
- Ⓖ distance
- Ⓗ disttance

© Macmillan/McGraw-Hill

Name_____

Read each sentence. If an underlined word is spelled wrong, fill in the circle that goes with that word. If no word is spelled wrong, fill in the circle below NONE. Read Sample A and do Sample B.

NONE

A. Don't <u>friten</u> the <u>captain</u> with your <u>signal</u>.   **A.** Ⓐ Ⓑ Ⓒ Ⓓ
        A   B   C

NONE

B. It would be my <u>pleasure</u> to give a <u>lecture</u> in the <u>footcher</u>.   **B.** Ⓔ Ⓕ Ⓖ Ⓗ
                 E   F   G

NONE

1. A <u>sandel</u> is not a <u>practical</u> <u>mountain</u>-climbing shoe.   **1.** Ⓐ Ⓑ Ⓒ Ⓓ
       A   B   C

NONE

2. <u>Listen</u>, ignore the <u>pressure</u>, and just enjoy the <u>contist</u>.   **2.** Ⓔ Ⓕ Ⓖ Ⓗ
     E   F   G

NONE

3. Scientists <u>measure</u> the amounts of <u>moysture</u> and   **3.** Ⓐ Ⓑ Ⓒ Ⓓ
           A   B

<u>pressure</u> in storms.
  C

NONE

4. The <u>lecture</u> was about the <u>importans</u> of good <u>balance</u>.   **4.** Ⓔ Ⓕ Ⓖ Ⓗ
       E   F   G

NONE

5. "Always <u>listen</u> to <u>natchure</u>" is my <u>slogan</u>.   **5.** Ⓐ Ⓑ Ⓒ Ⓓ
        A   B   C

NONE

6. The <u>absinse</u> of clouds revealed an <u>azure</u> sky in <u>nature</u>.   **6.** Ⓔ Ⓕ Ⓖ Ⓗ
       E   F   G

NONE

7. I hope he will not <u>refuse</u> to <u>cundukt</u> <u>research</u>.   **7.** Ⓐ Ⓑ Ⓒ Ⓓ
              A   B   C

NONE

8. In a <u>minute</u>, he will throw his <u>trowsurs</u> in the <u>laundry</u>.   **8.** Ⓔ Ⓕ Ⓖ Ⓗ
       E   F   G

NONE

9. The <u>captain</u> told us to use <u>cation</u> and not to be <u>rowdy</u>.   **9.** Ⓐ Ⓑ Ⓒ Ⓓ
       A   B   C

NONE

10. <u>Lissen</u> for a <u>minute</u> to hear if the <u>laundry</u> is done.   **10.** Ⓔ Ⓕ Ⓖ Ⓗ
     E   F   G

NONE

11. Who would put <u>trousers</u> and a <u>sandal</u> in the <u>landry</u>?   **11.** Ⓐ Ⓑ Ⓒ Ⓓ
            A   B   C

© Macmillan/McGraw-Hill

NONE

12. In the <u>future</u>, I will <u>refews</u> a <u>pretzel</u> if it is offered.   12. Ⓔ Ⓕ Ⓖ Ⓗ
       E   F   G

NONE

13. He was <u>grouchy</u> because the <u>shouer</u> had no <u>pressure</u>.   13. Ⓐ Ⓑ Ⓒ Ⓓ
               A   B   C

NONE

14. <u>Measure</u> the <u>distance</u> from here to the <u>mountin</u>.   14. Ⓔ Ⓕ Ⓖ Ⓗ
        E   F   G

NONE

15. It may be difficult to <u>conduct</u> <u>reesurch</u> in <u>August</u>.   15. Ⓐ Ⓑ Ⓒ Ⓓ
                            A   B   C

NONE

16. Please <u>excuse</u> my poor sense of <u>balence</u> and <u>distance</u>. 16. Ⓔ Ⓕ Ⓖ Ⓗ
            E   F   G

NONE

17. The <u>subject</u> of the president's <u>slogin</u> was <u>nature</u>.   17. Ⓐ Ⓑ Ⓒ Ⓓ
         A   B   C

NONE

18. Can you <u>meshure</u> the <u>importance</u> of a good <u>slogan</u>?   18. Ⓔ Ⓕ Ⓖ Ⓗ
            E   F   G

NONE

19. My <u>resadents</u> is on the <u>southern</u> side of the <u>mountain</u>. 19. Ⓐ Ⓑ Ⓒ Ⓓ
        A   B   C

NONE

20. What is the <u>distents</u> to the <u>treasure</u> near the <u>mountain</u>? 20. Ⓔ Ⓕ Ⓖ Ⓗ
                 E   F   G

NONE

21. In the <u>fable</u>, the girl ate her <u>pretsul</u> with great <u>pleasure</u>. 21. Ⓐ Ⓑ Ⓒ Ⓓ
            A   B   C

NONE

22. The characters were a <u>rebel</u>, a <u>rancher</u>, and a <u>cowerd</u>. 22. Ⓔ Ⓕ Ⓖ Ⓗ
                          E   F   G

NONE

23. We gazed at the <u>ashure</u> <u>August</u> sky with <u>pleasure</u>.   23. Ⓐ Ⓑ Ⓒ Ⓓ
                     A   B   C

NONE

24. They made the <u>grochy</u> Fisher lose his <u>balance</u> in less   24. Ⓔ Ⓕ Ⓖ Ⓗ
                   E   F

    than a <u>minute</u>.
            G

NONE

25. The <u>moisture</u> and <u>presher</u> were high near the <u>mountain</u>. 25. Ⓐ Ⓑ Ⓒ Ⓓ
         A   B   C

© Macmillan/McGraw-Hill

Name_____

Fold back the paper along the dotted line. Write the words in the blanks as they are read aloud. When you finish the test, unfold the paper. Use the list at the right to correct any spelling mistakes.

1. _____
2. _____
3. _____
4. _____
5. _____
6. _____
7. _____
8. _____
9. _____
10. _____
11. _____
12. _____
13. _____
14. _____
15. _____
16. _____
17. _____
18. _____
19. _____
20. _____

Review Words
21. _____
22. _____
23. _____

Challenge Words
24. _____
25. _____

1. margin
2. jolt
3. surge
4. plunge
5. jigsaw
6. legend
7. ridge
8. budge
9. lodge
10. agent
11. damage
12. ranger
13. jumble
14. managed
15. baggage
16. frigid
17. challenge
18. journal
19. judgment
20. knowledge
21. assistance
22. importance
23. absence
24. oxygen
25. surgeon

© Macmillan/McGraw-Hill

At Home: Help the student practice the words he or she missed to prepare for the Posttest.

Name_____

Using the Word Study Steps

1. LOOK at the word.
2. SAY the word aloud.
3. STUDY the letters in the word.
4. WRITE the word.

5. CHECK the word.
   Did you spell the word right?
   If not, go back to step 1.

Find and Circle

Find and circle each of the spelling words in this puzzle. Words may read forward, backward, upward, downward, or diagonally.

```
R F M T M B U D G E E E R E G N A R
I R A E N A C J S G G G D J U B R J
D I R G B E N Y K E N N R A J I I B
G G G D D A M A E J U E E V M G H J
E I I E J N G G G T L L H G S A U N
F D N L O M E G D E P L V A D M G W
R D U W L O D G A U D A W G B O V E
G V B O T C W C E G J H G L V W L M
A E I N A G E N T L E C E E G R U S
B W A K U B B G X J O U R N A L O A
```

List the words below as you find them in the puzzle.

1. _____
2. _____
3. _____
4. _____
5. _____
6. _____
7. _____

8. _____
9. _____
10. _____
11. _____
12. _____
13. _____
14. _____

15. _____
16. _____
17. _____
18. _____
19. _____
20. _____

At Home: Review the Word Study Steps above to help the student spell new words.

© Macmillan/McGraw-Hill

Name_____

challenge   agent   journal   legend
ridge   plunge   managed   lodge
margin   jumble   surge   jigsaw
knowledge   ranger   frigid   baggage
jolt   budge   damage   judgment

Sort each spelling word by finding the sound and spelling pattern to which it belongs. Write the spelling words that end with the soft *g* spelled:

-dge

1. _____

2. _____

3. _____

4. _____

Write the spelling words that begin with the soft *g* spelled:

j-

1. _____

2. _____

3. _____

4. _____

5. _____

Write the spelling words that end with the soft *g* spelled:

-ge

1. _____

2. _____

3. _____

4. _____

5. _____

6. _____

Write the spelling words that have the soft *g* in the middle spelled:

-ge

1. _____

2. _____

3. _____

-gi

1. _____

2. _____

© Macmillan/McGraw-Hill

Name_____

challenge	agent	journal	legend
ridge	plunge	managed	lodge
margin	jumble	surge	jigsaw
knowledge	ranger	frigid	baggage
jolt	budge	damage	judgment

Fill in the blanks

Complete each sentence with the correct spelling word.

1. The Antarctic weather was a _____ for Shackleton and his men.

2. The *Endurance* suffered _____ from the pressure of the ice floes.

3. Some sailors kept a _____ while at sea.

4. Working a _____ puzzle is a good way to pass the time.

5. Each _____ of cold ocean water soaked the boat and the sailors.

6. _____ of the sea and of fixing boats helped Shackleton's men stay safe.

7. They piled all of their belongings, or _____, on the ice.

8. Two lifeboats were used to make a _____ for shelter.

9. It must have felt great to cross the last _____ and see the whaling station.

10. Shackleton used good _____ when he said that they should leave the boat.

Synonyms

Write the spelling word that comes closest in meaning to each word below.

11. cold _____   15. fall _____   19. park worker

12. cause _____   16. bump _____   _____

13. mix up _____   17. edge _____   20. move

14. organized _____   18. story _____   _____

© Macmillan/McGraw-Hill

Name_____

Circle the misspelled words in the passage. Write the words correctly on the lines below.

  The men faced the challeng of sailing in the Antarctic with courage. They chopped ice from the boat to keep sailing. Their small boat already had damaje from a large surghe of icy water. Still, they manedged the largest waves. It was their goal to avoid any high crest or deep plundge. Their journey became a lejend of triumph over danger.

1. _____ 3. _____ 5. _____

2. _____ 4. _____ 6. _____

Writing Activity

Write a paragraph about a time when you or someone you know had to be brave. Use four words from your spelling list.

_____

_____

_____

_____

_____

_____

_____

_____

_____

_____

© Macmillan/McGraw-Hill

Name_____

Look at the words in each set below. One word in each set is
spelled correctly. Use a pencil to fill in the circle next to the correct
word. Before you begin, look at the sample set of words. Sample
A has been done for you. Do Sample B by yourself. When you are
sure you know what to do, you may go on with the rest of the page.

Sample A:

Ⓐ bullge
Ⓑ bulge
Ⓒ bulje
Ⓓ buldge

Sample B:

Ⓔ rigid
Ⓕ riggid
Ⓖ rijjid
Ⓗ ridgid

1. Ⓐ ajent
   Ⓑ agent
   Ⓒ aggent
   Ⓓ aigent

2. Ⓔ bagage
   Ⓕ baggage
   Ⓖ bagguge
   Ⓗ baggadge

3. Ⓐ budge
   Ⓑ budje
   Ⓒ buge
   Ⓓ buhdge

4. Ⓔ chalenge
   Ⓕ challenje
   Ⓖ challunge
   Ⓗ challenge

5. Ⓐ damij
   Ⓑ dammage
   Ⓒ damage
   Ⓓ damadge

6. Ⓔ plunje
   Ⓕ plundge
   Ⓖ plunge
   Ⓗ plunnge

7. Ⓐ giggsaw
   Ⓑ jiggsaw
   Ⓒ gigsaw
   Ⓓ jigsaw

8. Ⓔ jolt
   Ⓕ golt
   Ⓖ giolt
   Ⓗ jollt

9. Ⓐ jernal
   Ⓑ journal
   Ⓒ gournal
   Ⓓ gernal

10. Ⓔ judjment
    Ⓕ jujment
    Ⓖ jugment
    Ⓗ judgment

11. Ⓐ jumble
    Ⓑ jumbel
    Ⓒ jumbul
    Ⓓ gumble

12. Ⓔ knowlege
    Ⓕ nowledge
    Ⓖ knowledge
    Ⓗ knowlledge

13. Ⓐ lojje
    Ⓑ ladge
    Ⓒ logge
    Ⓓ lodge

14. Ⓔ managed
    Ⓕ maneged
    Ⓖ manijed
    Ⓗ manejd

15. Ⓐ margein
    Ⓑ marjin
    Ⓒ margin
    Ⓓ marjein

16. Ⓔ lejjend
    Ⓕ leggend
    Ⓖ lejend
    Ⓗ legend

17. Ⓐ ranger
    Ⓑ ranjer
    Ⓒ rangger
    Ⓓ raneger

18. Ⓔ ridge
    Ⓕ rigge
    Ⓖ ridje
    Ⓗ rijje

19. Ⓐ surje
    Ⓑ surge
    Ⓒ serge
    Ⓓ serje

20. Ⓔ frijid
    Ⓕ frigged
    Ⓖ frigid
    Ⓗ frijjed

© Macmillan/McGraw-Hill

Name_____

Fold back the paper along the dotted line. Write the words in the blanks as they are read aloud. When you finish the test, unfold the paper. Use the list at the right to correct any spelling mistakes.

1. _____
2. _____
3. _____
4. _____
5. _____
6. _____
7. _____
8. _____
9. _____
10. _____
11. _____
12. _____
13. _____
14. _____
15. _____
16. _____
17. _____
18. _____
19. _____
20. _____

Review Words 21. _____
22. _____
23. _____

Challenge Words 24. _____
25. _____

1. sweet
2. peel
3. peer
4. pole
5. poll
6. peal
7. waste
8. manner
9. current
10. manor
11. pier
12. waist
13. currant
14. presents
15. counsel
16. presence
17. council
18. stationary
19. stationery
20. suite
21. journal
22. budge
23. ranger
24. kernel
25. colonel

© Macmillan/McGraw-Hill

At Home: Help the student practice the words he or she missed to prepare for the Posttest.

Name_____

Using the Word Study Steps

1. LOOK at the word.
2. SAY the word aloud.
3. STUDY the letters in the word.

4. WRITE the word.
5. CHECK the word.
   Did you spell the word right?
   If not, go back to step 1.

Fill-Ins

Fill in the missing letters of each word to form a spelling word.

1. su____ ____e
2. sw____ ____t
3. p____ ____r
4. p____ ____r
5. cur____en____
6. curr____ ____t
7. man____ ____r

8. ma____ ____r
9. po____e
10. pol____
11. station____ ____y
12. stati____ ____er____
13. wai____ ____
14. was____ ____

15. pe____ ____
16. p____e____
17. prese____ ____s
18. pre____e____c____
19. coun____i____
20. cou____s____l

Make a Puzzle

Make up a puzzle of your own using the space on this page. Give it to someone else to solve. Be sure to include at least five spelling words in your puzzle.

At Home: Review the Word Study Steps above to help the student spell new words.

© Macmillan/McGraw-Hill

Name

poll   council   waist   manor
presents   current   peer   suite
stationary sweet   manner   currant
counsel   peal   presence   pier
peel   stationery   pole   waste

Sort each spelling word according to its number of syllables. Then write the words on the lines below.

One syllable

1. _____
2. _____
3. _____
4. _____
5. _____
6. _____
7. _____
8. _____
9. _____
10. _____

Two syllables

1. _____
2. _____
3. _____
4. _____
5. _____
6. _____
7. _____
8. _____

Four syllables

1. _____
2. _____

Use the spelling words above to help you write a poem of at least 4 lines.

1. _____
2. _____
3. _____
4. _____

© Macmillan/McGraw-Hill

Name_____

poll	council	waist	manor
presents	current	peer	suite
stationary	sweet	manner	currant
counsel	peal	presence	pier
peel	stationery	pole	waste

What's the Word?

Complete each sentence with the correct spelling word.

1. Wesley used the leaves of his plant to make _____ for writing letters.

2. The fruit in Weslandia was yellow in color and tasted _____.

3. Wesley helped the plant grow around a _____ to keep it from falling down.

4. Wesley used everything that grew in Weslandia, so there was never any

   _____.

5. Wesley's parents heard a _____ of laughter coming from behind the plant.

6. Busy in the world of Weslandia, Wesley lost track of _____ events.

7. Wesley used to be scared in the _____ of older boys.

8. The boys in the neighborhood wanted to help form a _____ for Weslandia.

9. Before creating Weslandia, Wesley always acted in a shy, quiet

   _____.

10. In his swing, Wesley was able to _____ around the corner without being seen.

© Macmillan/McGraw-Hill

Name_____

Circle the misspelled words in the passage. Write the words correctly on the lines below.

Wesley never exercised, and his mannor of dieting was poor. Luckily, the fruits that he grew were not only suite but healthful, too. To his surprise, he could even eat the peal. Within a few weeks, his waste shrank by two inches. The boys who had teased him before now came and sought his counsil. People in the neighborhood went out of their way just to be in his presents.

1. _____   3. _____   5. _____

2. _____   4. _____   6. _____

Writing Activity

Write a paragraph about a summer project that you would like to try. Use four words from your spelling list.

_____

_____

_____

_____

_____

_____

_____

_____

_____

_____

_____

_____

_____

© Macmillan/McGraw-Hill

Look at the words in each set below. One word in each set is spelled correctly. Use a pencil to fill in the circle next to the correct word. Before you begin, look at the sample set of words. Sample A has been done for you. Do Sample B by yourself. When you are sure you know what to do, you may go on with the rest of the page.

Sample A:

Ⓐ flowr
Ⓑ flour
Ⓒ flouer
Ⓓ flauer

Sample B:

Ⓔ flower
Ⓕ flowr
Ⓖ flouwer
Ⓗ flowwer

1. Ⓐ suitte
   Ⓑ suite
   Ⓒ suete
   Ⓓ suette

2. Ⓔ sweet
   Ⓕ swete
   Ⓖ swet
   Ⓗ swette

3. Ⓐ peire
   Ⓑ piere
   Ⓒ peir
   Ⓓ pier

4. Ⓔ peer
   Ⓕ pere
   Ⓖ perre
   Ⓗ peere

5. Ⓐ curant
   Ⓑ currant
   Ⓒ currannt
   Ⓓ currantt

6. Ⓔ current
   Ⓕ curent
   Ⓖ currennt
   Ⓗ curennt

7. Ⓐ mannir
   Ⓑ mannur
   Ⓒ maner
   Ⓓ manner

8. Ⓔ mannor
   Ⓕ manor
   Ⓖ mannour
   Ⓗ manur

9. Ⓐ poal
   Ⓑ pollel
   Ⓒ pole
   Ⓓ poel

10. Ⓔ poll
    Ⓕ pol
    Ⓖ polle
    Ⓗ poell

11. Ⓐ stationarry
    Ⓑ stationary
    Ⓒ staitionary
    Ⓓ staytionary

12. Ⓔ stationery
    Ⓕ staytionery
    Ⓖ staitionery
    Ⓗ stationerry

13. Ⓐ wastte
    Ⓑ wasste
    Ⓒ waiste
    Ⓓ waste

14. Ⓔ waist
    Ⓕ waiset
    Ⓖ waiste
    Ⓗ waisst

15. Ⓐ peale
    Ⓑ peal
    Ⓒ peall
    Ⓓ peil

16. Ⓔ peell
    Ⓕ peel
    Ⓖ peele
    Ⓗ peelle

17. Ⓐ pressunts
    Ⓑ presunts
    Ⓒ pressents
    Ⓓ presents

18. Ⓔ pressence
    Ⓕ presence
    Ⓖ presense
    Ⓗ presensce

19. Ⓐ counncil
    Ⓑ council
    Ⓒ counccil
    Ⓓ counsil

20. Ⓔ counsel
    Ⓕ counssel
    Ⓖ counsell
    Ⓗ counssell

© Macmillan/McGraw-Hill

Name_____

Fold back the paper along the dotted line. Write the words in the blanks as they are read aloud. When you finish the test, unfold the paper. Use the list at the right to correct any spelling mistakes.

1. _____
2. _____
3. _____
4. _____
5. _____
6. _____
7. _____
8. _____
9. _____
10. _____
11. _____
12. _____
13. _____
14. _____
15. _____
16. _____
17. _____
18. _____
19. _____
20. _____

Review Words 21. _____

22. _____

23. _____

Challenge Words 24. _____

25. _____

1. prewash
2. disable
3. discolor
4. mistaken
5. preheats
6. mistrust
7. incorrect
8. disconnect
9. preview
10. prejudge
11. misjudge
12. discomfort
13. dismount
14. misunderstand
15. disobey
16. dishonest
17. injustice
18. disapprove
19. inexpensive
20. indefinite
21. presence
22. stationary
23. current
24. prehistoric
25. misbehave

© Macmillan/McGraw-Hill

At Home: Help the student practice the words he or she missed to prepare for the Posttest.

Spelling

Words with Prefixes
dis-, in-, mis-,
and *pre-*: Practice

Name_____

Using the Word Study Steps

1. LOOK at the word.
2. SAY the word aloud.
3. STUDY the letters in the word.

4. WRITE the word.
5. CHECK the word.
   Did you spell the word right?
   If not, go back to step 1.

Find and Circle

Find and circle each of the spelling words in this puzzle. Words may read forward, backward, upward, downward, or diagonally.

```
D P R E J U D G E S K G I E D D P L H E
Z I E C I T S U J N I L N V E I G U S T
I R S E G D U J S I M G C I V S G A A I
L I Z H P R E V I E W B O S O C E S W N
D W X D O D I S A B L E R N R O N T E I
R H X T N N A Y C D L F R E P M E A R F
Y D B O O J E C P J R N E P P F K E P E
Y E B O S I D S R E F G C X A O A H M D
D I S M O U N T T E N K T E S R T E D N
M I S U N D E R S T A N D N I T S R G I
T C E N N O C S I D U R N I D U I P K J
M I S T R U S T D I S C O L O R M D C A
```

List each of the words below as you find them in the puzzle.

1. _____
2. _____
3. _____
4. _____
5. _____
6. _____
7. _____

8. _____
9. _____
10. _____
11. _____
12. _____
13. _____
14. _____

15. _____
16. _____
17. _____
18. _____
19. _____
20. _____

© Macmillan/McGraw-Hill

At Home: Review the Word Study Steps above to help the student spell new words.

indefinite	disable	incorrect	dismount
preview	misunderstand	disobey	prewash
dishonest	inexpensive	prejudge	mistaken
disapprove	misjudge	discomfort	discolor
injustice	preheats	mistrust	disconnect

Sort each spelling word according to its prefix. Then write the words on the lines below.

dis-

1. _____
2. _____
3. _____
4. _____
5. _____
6. _____
7. _____
8. _____

in-

1. _____
2. _____
3. _____
4. _____

mis-

1. _____
2. _____
3. _____
4. _____

pre-

1. _____
2. _____
3. _____
4. _____

© Macmillan/McGraw-Hill

Name_____

indefinite	disable	incorrect	dismount
preview	misunderstand	disobey	prewash
dishonest	inexpensive	prejudge	mistaken
disapprove	misjudge	discomfort	discolor
injustice	preheats	mistrust	disconnect

Similar Meanings

Write the spelling word that has the same, or almost the same, meaning.

1. wrong _____

2. lying _____

3. unsure; unclear _____

4. cheap _____

5. frown on _____

6. go against the rules _____

7. stain _____

8. uneasiness _____

9. divide _____

10. get down or get off _____

Fill in the Blanks

Complete each sentence using the correct spelling word.

11. If you think that plants are not important to our survival, you are

    _____.

12. Since Lewis and Clark had no map, it was easy to _____ distances.

13. When Clark first saw the ocean, he had a _____ of what we see today.

14. Joseph Andrews once tried to _____ the machines that chop down trees.

15. The destruction of our natural environment is a real _____.

16. We should _____ anyone who wants to destroy our surroundings.

17. When you _____ your clothes, you use up more water.

18. His mother _____ the oven before cooking dinner.

© Macmillan/McGraw-Hill

Name_____

Circle the misspelled words in the passage. Write the words correctly on the lines below.

Many people are mistakin about what they can do to help protect nature. They think that the destruction of our environment is an injustis, but they don't know how they can help. In fact, there are plenty of easy and inexpencive ways to take action. Some people disobay recycling laws because they don't know any better! You can tell people who litter or pollute that you disaproove. Don't prejuge others, but take some time to learn what you can do to help.

1. _____ 3. _____ 5. _____

2. _____ 4. _____ 6. _____

Writing Activity

Write a paragraph about things that you can do to help protect nature in your area. Use four words from your spelling list.

_____
_____
_____
_____
_____
_____
_____
_____
_____
_____
_____
_____
_____

© Macmillan/McGraw-Hill

Name_____

Look at the words in each set below. One word in each set is spelled correctly. Use a pencil to fill in the circle next to the correct word. Before you begin, look at the sample set of words. Sample A has been done for you. Do Sample B by yourself. When you are sure you know what to do, you may go on with the rest of the page.

Sample A:

Ⓐ misshapp
Ⓑ mishapp
Ⓒ misshap
Ⓓ mishap ●

Sample B:

Ⓔ missuse
Ⓕ misuse
Ⓖ misusse
Ⓗ missusse

1. Ⓐ dissaprove
   Ⓑ disaprove
   Ⓒ dissapprove
   Ⓓ disapprove

6. Ⓔ misstakken
   Ⓕ mistakken
   Ⓖ misstaken
   Ⓗ mistaken

11. Ⓐ preheats
    Ⓑ preaheats
    Ⓒ prehheats
    Ⓓ preheets

16. Ⓔ discollor
    Ⓕ disccolor
    Ⓖ disscolor
    Ⓗ discolor

2. Ⓔ discomfert
   Ⓕ disscomfort
   Ⓖ discomfort
   Ⓗ discommfort

7. Ⓐ mistrust
   Ⓑ misstrust
   Ⓒ misttrust
   Ⓓ mistrustt

12. Ⓔ inexpensive
    Ⓕ innexpensive
    Ⓖ inexppensive
    Ⓗ inexpenssive

17. Ⓐ disconnect
    Ⓑ disconect
    Ⓒ disconnecct
    Ⓓ dissconnect

3. Ⓐ dishonnest
   Ⓑ disshonest
   Ⓒ dishonest
   Ⓓ disshonnest

8. Ⓔ misundderstand
   Ⓕ missunderstand
   Ⓖ misunderstand
   Ⓗ misundderstand

13. Ⓐ injjustice
    Ⓑ injustice
    Ⓒ injustisce
    Ⓓ injusstic

18. Ⓔ missjudge
    Ⓕ misjudge
    Ⓖ misjuge
    Ⓗ misjudje

4. Ⓔ dismount
   Ⓕ dissmount
   Ⓖ dismmount
   Ⓗ dissmmount

9. Ⓐ incorect
   Ⓑ incorrect
   Ⓒ incorreckt
   Ⓓ inccorrect

14. Ⓔ indefinnite
    Ⓕ indeffinite
    Ⓖ inddefinite
    Ⓗ indefinite

19. Ⓐ prejudje
    Ⓑ prejudge
    Ⓒ preejudge
    Ⓓ prejuge

5. Ⓐ dissobey
   Ⓑ disobey
   Ⓒ disobbey
   Ⓓ dissobbey

10. Ⓔ prevview
    Ⓕ prevewe
    Ⓖ prevew
    Ⓗ preview

15. Ⓐ disabel
    Ⓑ dissable
    Ⓒ disable
    Ⓓ dissabble

20. Ⓔ prewwash
    Ⓕ preewash
    Ⓖ prewash
    Ⓗ prewassh

© Macmillan/McGraw-Hill

Name_____

Fold back the paper along the dotted line. Write the words in the blanks as they are read aloud. When you finish the test, unfold the paper. Use the list at the right to correct any spelling mistakes.

1. _____
2. _____
3. _____
4. _____
5. _____
6. _____
7. _____
8. _____
9. _____
10. _____
11. _____
12. _____
13. _____
14. _____
15. _____
16. _____
17. _____
18. _____
19. _____
20. _____

Review Words 21. _____

22. _____

23. _____

Challenge Words 24. _____

25. _____

1. sadness
2. gladness
3. needless
4. harmless
5. darkness
6. fullness
7. stillness
8. hopeless
9. fearless
10. weakness
11. bottomless
12. foolishness
13. fondness
14. effortless
15. meaningless
16. emptiness
17. forgiveness
18. motionless
19. ceaseless
20. fierceness
21. dishonest
22. mistaken
23. preheat
24. weightlessness
25. thoughtlessness

© Macmillan/McGraw-Hill

At Home: Help the student practice the words he or she missed to prepare for the Posttest.

The Unbreakable Code

Name_____

Using the Word Study Steps

1. LOOK at the word.

2. SAY the word aloud.

3. STUDY the letters in the word.

4. WRITE the word.

5. CHECK the word.
   Did you spell the word right?
   If not, go back to step 1.

Fill-Ins

Fill in the missing letters of each word to form a spelling word.

1. bottom___ ___ ___s

2. cease___ ___ ___s

3. dark___ ___ ___s

4. effort___ ___ ___s

5. empt___ ___ ___ss

6. fea___ ___ess

7. fierc___n___ ___s

8. fon___ ___es___

9. fooli___ ___ ___ess

10. forgiv___ ___ess

11. ful___n___ ___s

12. hope___ ___ss

13. gla___ ___ess

14. mean___ng___ ___ss

15. har___ ___ess

16. moti___ ___l___ss

17. need___ ___ss

18. sti___l___e___s

19. sa___n___s___

20. wea___ ___es___

Use the spelling words above to write a poem of at least 4 lines.

1. _____

2. _____

3. _____

4. _____

At Home: Review the Word Study Steps above to help the
student spell new words.

© Macmillan/McGraw-Hill

Name_____

emptiness	fullness	motionless	hopeless
gladness	fierceness	stillness	ceaseless
bottomless	darkness	sadness	weakness
foolishness	effortless	needless	meaningless
harmless	forgiveness	fearless	fondness

Sort each spelling word by its suffix. On the lines below, write the spelling words with the -*less* suffix that have:

two syllables

1. _____

2. _____

3. _____

4. _____

5. _____

three syllables

1. _____

2. _____

3. _____

4. _____

Write the spelling words with the -*ness* suffix that have:

two syllables

1. _____

2. _____

3. _____

4. _____

5. _____

6. _____

7. _____

8. _____

three syllables

1. _____

2. _____

3. _____

Find the two spelling words that rhyme and write them on the lines below.

1. _____   2. _____

© Macmillan/McGraw-Hill

Name_____

emptiness	fullness	motionless	hopeless
gladness	fierceness	stillness	ceaseless
bottomless	darkness	sadness	weakness
foolishness	effortless	needless	meaningless
harmless	forgiveness	fearless	fondness

Definitions

Write the spelling word that comes closest in meaning to the words below.

1. still; not moving _____

2. impossible; without a chance

_____

3. happiness _____

4. unafraid _____

5. not stopping _____

6. unnecessary _____

7. the absence of light

_____

8. not requiring energy

_____

9. causing little or no hurt

_____

10. love; affection _____

Fill in the Blanks

Complete the sentences, using the correct spelling word.

11. John's grandfather felt like he was in a _____ canyon.

12. When John's grandfather saw the dead soldiers, he was filled with

_____.

13. After the battle, there was an eerie _____ on the field.

14. The Navajo language was _____ to the Japanese, who didn't speak it.

15. John began to appreciate the _____ of the soldiers.

16. The _____ of the battlefield showed that the war had long been over.

© Macmillan/McGraw-Hill

Name _____

Circle the misspelled words in the passage. Write the words correctly on the lines below.

The soldiers stood moshunless in the field. What was so important about a harmliss code? As the darknes crept in, they felt alone. An emptyness came over them as they waited. The mission seemed meaninglis to them. They had no idea that the language they knew so well would play a key part in the weekness of the Japanese army!

1. _____   3. _____   5. _____

2. _____   4. _____   6. _____

Writing Activity

Write a paragraph about what you would do if you had a code of your own. Use four words from your spelling list.

_____

_____

_____

_____

_____

_____

_____

_____

_____

_____

_____

_____

© Macmillan/McGraw-Hill

Name_____

Look at the words in each set below. One word in each set is
spelled correctly. Use a pencil to fill in the circle next to the correct
word. Before you begin, look at the sample set of words. Sample
A has been done for you. Do Sample B by yourself. When you are
sure you know what to do, you may go on with the rest of the page.

Sample A:

Ⓐ useless
Ⓑ usseless
Ⓒ uselless
Ⓓ ueseless

Sample B:

Ⓔ hapyness
Ⓕ happyness
Ⓖ hapiness
Ⓗ happiness

1. Ⓐ botomless
   Ⓑ bottommless
   Ⓒ bottomless
   Ⓓ botommless

6. Ⓔ fearlless
   Ⓕ fearless
   Ⓖ feerless
   Ⓗ fereless

11. Ⓐ fullness
    Ⓑ fulness
    Ⓒ fullnness
    Ⓓ fulnness

16. Ⓔ motionlless
    Ⓕ motionnless
    Ⓖ mottionless
    Ⓗ motionless

2. Ⓔ ceaselless
   Ⓕ ceasless
   Ⓖ ceaseless
   Ⓗ ceeseless

7. Ⓐ fiercenness
   Ⓑ feirceness
   Ⓒ fierceness
   Ⓓ feircenness

12. Ⓔ hopelless
    Ⓕ hopeless
    Ⓖ hopless
    Ⓗ hoppeless

17. Ⓐ needlless
    Ⓑ needeless
    Ⓒ needless
    Ⓓ neadless

3. Ⓐ darknness
   Ⓑ darkness
   Ⓒ darknes
   Ⓓ darkkness

8. Ⓔ fonddnness
   Ⓕ fondnness
   Ⓖ fonddness
   Ⓗ fondness

13. Ⓐ gladdnness
    Ⓑ gladness
    Ⓒ gladdness
    Ⓓ gladness

18. Ⓔ stillness
    Ⓕ stilness
    Ⓖ stillnness
    Ⓗ stilnness

4. Ⓔ efortlless
   Ⓕ effortlless
   Ⓖ efortless
   Ⓗ effortless

9. Ⓐ foolishness
   Ⓑ foollishness
   Ⓒ foolishnness
   Ⓓ foollishnness

14. Ⓔ meaninglless
    Ⓕ meaningless
    Ⓖ meaningless
    Ⓗ meaninggless

19. Ⓐ sadnness
    Ⓑ saddness
    Ⓒ sadness
    Ⓓ saddnness

5. Ⓐ emptynness
   Ⓑ emptinness
   Ⓒ epmtyness
   Ⓓ emptiness

10. Ⓔ forgiveness
    Ⓕ forggiveness
    Ⓖ forgivenness
    Ⓗ foregiveness

15. Ⓐ harmmless
    Ⓑ harmless
    Ⓒ harmlless
    Ⓓ harrmless

20. Ⓔ weekness
    Ⓕ weakness
    Ⓖ weakeness
    Ⓗ weaknness

© Macmillan/McGraw-Hill

Name<u>   </u>

Fold back the paper along the dotted line. Write the words in the blanks as they are read aloud. When you finish the test, unfold the paper. Use the list at the right to correct any spelling mistakes.

1. <u>   </u>
2. <u>   </u>
3. <u>   </u>
4. <u>   </u>
5. <u>   </u>
6. <u>   </u>
7. <u>   </u>
8. <u>   </u>
9. <u>   </u>
10. <u>   </u>
11. <u>   </u>
12. <u>   </u>
13. <u>   </u>
14. <u>   </u>
15. <u>   </u>
16. <u>   </u>
17. <u>   </u>
18. <u>   </u>
19. <u>   </u>
20. <u>   </u>

Review Words 21. <u>   </u>
22. <u>   </u>
23. <u>   </u>

Challenge Words 24. <u>   </u>
25. <u>   </u>

1. impress
2. correct
3. elect
4. discuss
5. locate
6. decorate
7. confuse
8. estimate
9. impression
10. correction
11. election
12. discussion
13. location
14. decoration
15. confusion
16. estimation
17. concentrate
18. exhaust
19. concentration
20. exhaustion
21. hopeless
22. fearless
23. forgiveness
24. conclude
25. conclusion

© Macmillan/McGraw-Hill

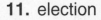 **At Home:** Help the student practice the words he or she missed to prepare for the Posttest.

Using the Word Study Steps

1. LOOK at the word.

2. SAY the word aloud.

3. STUDY the letters in the word.

4. WRITE the word.

5. CHECK the word.
   Did you spell the word right?
   If not, go back to step 1.

Fill-Ins

Fill in the missing letters of each word to form a spelling word.

1. disc____ ____s

2. loca____ ____

3. imp____ ____ss

4. el____ ____t

5. elect____ ____n

6. correc____ ____on

7. decor____ ____e

8. confusi____ ____

9. concentrati____ ____

10. concentra____ ____

11. discus____ ____on

12. loca____ ____ ____n

13. impress____ ____ ____

14. corre____ ____

15. confu____ ____

16. decora____ ____on

17. estim____ ____ion

18. exhau____ ____

19. exhaust____ ____ ____

20. estim____ ____e

Alphabetical Order

Use the lines below to write the spelling words in alphabetical order.

1. _____ 6. _____ 11. _____ 16. _____

2. _____ 7. _____ 12. _____ 17. _____

3. _____ 8. _____ 13. _____ 18. _____

4. _____ 9. _____ 14. _____ 19. _____

5. _____ 10. _____ 15. _____ 20. _____

At Home: Review the Word Study Steps above to help the student spell new words.

© Macmillan/McGraw-Hill

Name _____

exhaustion   impression   location   elect
decoration   discussion   discuss   correct
election   confuse   estimation   confusion
impress   concentration correction   concentrate
locate   exhaust   decorate   estimate

Sort each spelling word by finding the sound and spelling pattern to which it belongs. Write the spelling words with the ending spelled:

-ate

1. _____
2. _____
3. _____
4. _____

-ct

1. _____
2. _____

-ss

1. _____
2. _____

Write the spelling words with the ending spelled:

-se

1. _____

-st

1. _____

-tion

1. _____
2. _____
3. _____
4. _____

5. _____
6. _____
7. _____

-sion

1. _____
2. _____
3. _____

© Macmillan/McGraw-Hill

Name_____

exhaustion	impression	location	elect
decoration	discussion	discuss	correct
election	confuse	estimation	confusion
impress	concentration	correction	concentrate
locate	exhaust	decorate	estimate

Meaning Match

Write the spelling word that matches each clue below.

1. the state of being tired

   _____

2. the act of thinking _____

3. to guess _____

4. the result of voting _____

5. to find _____

6. an opinion _____

7. to talk _____

8. to have a strong effect on

   _____

9. a place _____

10. the act of making right

    _____

Fill in the Blanks

Complete each sentence with a spelling word.

11. Ana Rosa goes inside because when she works she needs to

    _____.

12. At first, there was some _____ about the truth behind the sea monster.

13. His Jeep blew _____ into the air.

14. No one had time to _____ the porch for the planning meeting.

15. Our first _____ was that it was a sea monster.

16. They decided to _____ someone to watch from the tree.

17. Their _____ about the sea monster lasted into the night.

18. Ana Rosa was _____ about there being something in the water.

© Macmillan/McGraw-Hill

Circle the misspelled words in the passage. Write the words correctly on the lines below.

　　　Ana Rosa climbed up the gri gri tree in order to concentrayt. It was a perfect locasion for watching the ocean. One day, Ana Rosa saw something that broke her consentrasion: a sea monster! At first no one believed her, but then it turned out that she was correcte. People met to diskus the sea monster. Their discustion lasted late into the night.

1. _____　3. _____　5. _____

2. _____　4. _____　6. _____

Writing Activity

Write a paragraph about a time when you or a person you know planned an event or an activity. Use four words from your spelling list.

_____

_____

_____

_____

_____

_____

_____

_____

_____

_____

_____

_____

© Macmillan/McGraw-Hill

Name_____

Look at the words in each set below. One word in each set is
spelled correctly. Use a pencil to fill in the circle next to the correct
word. Before you begin, look at the sample set of words. Sample
A has been done for you. Do Sample B by yourself. When you are
sure you know what to do, you may go on with the rest of the page.

Sample A:

Ⓐ edditt
Ⓑ eddit
Ⓒ edit
Ⓓ editt

Sample B:

Ⓔ eddition
Ⓕ edition
Ⓖ edittion
Ⓗ eddittion

1. Ⓐ concentrate
   Ⓑ conncentrate
   Ⓒ concenntrate
   Ⓓ concentratte

6. Ⓔ corection
   Ⓕ correction
   Ⓖ correcktion
   Ⓗ corecktion

11. Ⓐ esttimate
    Ⓑ esstimate
    Ⓒ estimmate
    Ⓓ estimate

16. Ⓔ imppresion
    Ⓕ impresion
    Ⓖ immpression
    Ⓗ impression

2. Ⓔ concetration
   Ⓕ concentration
   Ⓖ conncetration
   Ⓗ conncentration

7. Ⓐ deccorrate
   Ⓑ decorrate
   Ⓒ deccorate
   Ⓓ decorate

12. Ⓔ estimmation
    Ⓕ esttimmation
    Ⓖ esttimation
    Ⓗ estimation

17. Ⓐ locate
    Ⓑ loccate
    Ⓒ locatte
    Ⓓ loccatte

3. Ⓐ confusse
   Ⓑ connffuse
   Ⓒ conffuse
   Ⓓ confuse

8. Ⓔ decorration
   Ⓕ deccoration
   Ⓖ deccorration
   Ⓗ decoration

13. Ⓐ exaust
    Ⓑ exhaust
    Ⓒ exxhaust
    Ⓓ exhaustt

18. Ⓔ loccation
    Ⓕ location
    Ⓖ locattion
    Ⓗ loccattion

4. Ⓔ confusion
   Ⓕ conffusion
   Ⓖ confussion
   Ⓗ conffussion

9. Ⓐ ellect
   Ⓑ elect
   Ⓒ eleckt
   Ⓓ elleckt

14. Ⓔ exaustion
    Ⓕ exxhaution
    Ⓖ exhaustion
    Ⓗ exxaution

19. Ⓐ discusss
    Ⓑ disscus
    Ⓒ disscuss
    Ⓓ discuss

5. Ⓐ correct
   Ⓑ corect
   Ⓒ correckt
   Ⓓ coreckt

10. Ⓔ election
    Ⓕ ellection
    Ⓖ elecktion
    Ⓗ ellecktion

15. Ⓐ impress
    Ⓑ immpress
    Ⓒ imppress
    Ⓓ impres

20. Ⓔ discussion
    Ⓕ discusion
    Ⓖ disscussion
    Ⓗ disccussion

© Macmillan/McGraw-Hill

Name_____

Read each sentence. If an underlined word is spelled wrong, fill in the circle that goes with that word. If no word is spelled wrong, fill in the circle below NONE. Read Sample A and do Sample B.

NONE

A. He had a <u>fondness</u> for starting a <u>needlis</u> <u>discussion</u>.   A. Ⓐ ⬤ Ⓒ Ⓓ
          A   B   C

NONE

B. I <u>challenge</u> you to try to <u>confyuse</u> the <u>ranger</u>.   B. Ⓔ Ⓕ Ⓖ Ⓗ
      E   F   G

NONE

1. Her <u>jurnal</u> told of the <u>confusion</u> and <u>damage</u>.   1. Ⓐ Ⓑ Ⓒ Ⓓ
    A   B   C

NONE

2. The <u>peel</u> of the fruit was <u>harmliss</u>, and even <u>sweet</u>.   2. Ⓔ Ⓕ Ⓖ Ⓗ
    E   F   G

NONE

3. <u>Curant</u> information shows our <u>estimate</u> to be <u>incorrect</u>.   3. Ⓐ Ⓑ Ⓒ Ⓓ
   A   B   C

NONE

4. It is an <u>injustice</u> to <u>disobey</u> people with so much <u>knolege</u>.   4. Ⓔ Ⓕ Ⓖ Ⓗ
      E   F   G

NONE

5. The real <u>challenge</u> will be to <u>estamate</u> the <u>correct</u> answer.   5. Ⓐ Ⓑ Ⓒ Ⓓ
       A   B   C

NONE

6. Please <u>consintrate</u>, and try to <u>locate</u> that <u>pole</u>.   6. Ⓔ Ⓕ Ⓖ Ⓗ
      E   F   G

NONE

7. The <u>plunge</u> seemed <u>harmless</u>, but caused <u>damadge</u> to   7. Ⓐ Ⓑ Ⓒ Ⓓ
     A   B   C
the ship.

NONE

8. Their <u>incorrect</u> <u>knowledge</u> of whales was their <u>weekness</u>.   8. Ⓔ Ⓕ Ⓖ Ⓗ
        E   F   G

NONE

9. You're <u>mistaken</u> if you think <u>forgivniss</u> is <u>meaningless</u>.   9. Ⓐ Ⓑ Ⓒ Ⓓ
        A   B   C

NONE

10. The <u>preevew</u> showed their attempt to <u>locate</u> the North <u>Pole</u>. 10. Ⓔ Ⓕ Ⓖ Ⓗ
      E   F   G

NONE

11. In the <u>legend</u>, John sat <u>moshonless</u>, asking for   11. Ⓐ Ⓑ Ⓒ Ⓓ
      A   B
<u>forgiveness</u>.
  C

© Macmillan/McGraw-Hill

Name_____

12. Our <u>current</u> goal is <u>meeningles</u>, and I <u>disapprove</u>.
       E   F   G

12. Ⓔ Ⓕ Ⓖ Ⓗ   NONE

13. He wrote about the <u>swete</u> fruit in the <u>margin</u> of his <u>journal</u>.
                        A   B   C

13. Ⓐ Ⓑ Ⓒ Ⓓ   NONE

14. You are <u>misteaken</u> if you think I will <u>disobey</u> <u>current</u> orders.
             E   F   G

14. Ⓔ Ⓕ Ⓖ Ⓗ   NONE

15. It's a <u>waiste</u> to try to <u>impress</u> me or cure my <u>sadness</u>.
          A   B   C

15. Ⓐ Ⓑ Ⓒ Ⓓ   NONE

16. I <u>challenge</u> you to <u>lockate</u> the <u>correct</u> position of the ship.
      E   F   G

16. Ⓔ Ⓕ Ⓖ Ⓗ   NONE

17. His <u>weakness</u> is an <u>injustice</u>, and I strongly <u>dissaproove</u>.
        A   B   C

17. Ⓐ Ⓑ Ⓒ Ⓓ   NONE

18. It's a <u>waste</u> of time to sit there <u>motionless</u>, refusing to
         E   F

18. Ⓔ Ⓕ Ⓖ Ⓗ   NONE

<u>peyl</u> the fruit.
G

19. It was a real <u>chalinge</u> to <u>concentrate</u> on the <u>preview</u>.
               A   B   C

19. Ⓐ Ⓑ Ⓒ Ⓓ   NONE

20. The <u>legend</u> stated that the crew's <u>plunje</u> was <u>harmless</u>.
      E   F   G

20. Ⓔ Ⓕ Ⓖ Ⓗ   NONE

21. Your <u>estimate</u> is <u>incurrect</u> and <u>meaningless</u>.
        A   B   C

21. Ⓐ Ⓑ Ⓒ Ⓓ   NONE

22. The <u>judgment</u> caused <u>confushun</u> and then <u>sadness</u>.
        E   F   G

22. Ⓔ Ⓕ Ⓖ Ⓗ   NONE

23. His <u>journal</u> had an <u>estimate</u> of the North <u>Poll</u>'s size.
        A   B   C

23. Ⓐ Ⓑ Ⓒ Ⓓ   NONE

24. In <u>weakness</u> and <u>confusion</u>, she lost the <u>curreckt</u> map.
     E   F   G

24. Ⓔ Ⓕ Ⓖ Ⓗ   NONE

25. The misuse of <u>waste</u> in our environment is an
              A

25. Ⓐ Ⓑ Ⓒ Ⓓ   NONE

<u>enjustice</u>, and I <u>disapprove</u>.
 B   C

© Macmillan/McGraw-Hill

Name _____

Fold back the paper along the dotted line. Write the words in the blanks as they are read aloud. When you finish the test, unfold the paper. Use the list at the right to correct any spelling mistakes.

1. _____
2. _____
3. _____
4. _____
5. _____
6. _____
7. _____
8. _____
9. _____
10. _____
11. _____
12. _____
13. _____
14. _____
15. _____
16. _____
17. _____
18. _____
19. _____
20. _____

Review Words   21. _____
22. _____
23. _____

Challenge Words 24. _____
25. _____

1. astronaut
2. autograph
3. automatic
4. automobile
5. mythical
6. telegraph
7. telephone
8. telescope
9. television
10. telegram
11. homophone
12. phonics
13. disaster
14. astronomer
15. photograph
16. photography
17. myth
18. mechanic
19. mechanical
20. telephoto
21. correction
22. discussion
23. decoration
24. videophone
25. photogenic

© Macmillan/McGraw-Hill

At Home: Help the student practice the words he or she missed to prepare for the Posttest.

Name_____

Using the Word Study Steps

1. LOOK at the word.
2. SAY the word aloud.
3. STUDY the letters in the word.

4. WRITE the word.
5. CHECK the word.
   Did you spell the word right?
   If not, go back to step 1.

Fill-Ins

Fill in the missing letters of each word to form a spelling word.

1. a ____ t ____ onaut
2. a ____ t ____ graph
3. aut ____ m ____ tic
4. a ____ to ____ ____ bile
5. m ____ ____ hical
6. ____ e ____ egraph
7. t ____ l ____ phone
8. ____ el ____ ____ cope
9. te ____ ____ ____ ision
10. te ____ eg ____ am

11. hom ____ ____ h ____ ne
12. p ____ o ____ ics
13. di ____ a ____ ____ er
14. ____ st ____ ____ nomer
15. p ____ ____ t ____ graph
16. ____ ____ otogr ____ phy
17. m ____ ____ h
18. me ____ ____ an ____ c
19. ____ ec ____ anic ____ l
20. t ____ le ____ ____ oto

Make a Puzzle

Make up a puzzle of your own using the space on this page. Give it to someone else to solve. Be sure to include at least five spelling words in your puzzle.

At Home: Review the Word Study Steps above to help the student spell new words.

© Macmillan/McGraw-Hill

Name

telegram   automatic   homophone   myth
mechanic   disaster   telegraph   astronaut
automobile   telephoto   astronomer   photograph
photography   telescope   autograph   telephone
phonics   mechanical   television   mythical

**Sort each spelling word according to the Greek root it contains.
Then write the words on the lines below. Some words may be
placed into more than one category.**

astro   aster

1. _____   2. _____   3. _____

auto

1. _____   2. _____   3. _____

photo

1. _____   2. _____   3. _____

tele

1. _____   2. _____   3. _____
4. _____   5. _____   6. _____

phon

1. _____   2. _____   3. _____

mech

1. _____   2. _____

myth

1. _____   2. _____

© Macmillan/McGraw-Hill

Name_____

telegram	automatic	homophone	myth
mechanic	disaster	telegraph	astronaut
automobile	telephoto	astronomer	photograph
photography	telescope	autograph	telephone
phonics	mechanical	television	mythical

Complete each sentence below with a spelling word.

1. Alexi gazed up at the stars through his _____.

2. A _____ of the Tsar would have let Yelena the Fair see how old he was.

3. Alexi had no _____, so he had to travel on a horse.

4. The Golden Mare is a _____ creature.

5. The word "fair" is a _____ of "fare" because it sounds the same but is spelled differently.

6. If Alexi hadn't had the ring, it would have been a _____.

7. The Golden Mare told a _____ about how the ring was formed.

8. An _____ taught Alexi how to travel by using the stars.

9. The Tsar designed a _____ device for hunting birds.

10. The _____ was not yet invented at the time of the story.

Write On!

Use each spelling word in a sentence.

11. mechanic _____

12. television _____

13. astronaut _____

14. photography _____

15. autograph _____

© Macmillan/McGraw-Hill

Name_____

Circle the misspelled words in the passage. Write the words correctly on the lines below.

Andrea turned on the telivision. There was a program on about a mithical bird and a horse. She picked up the telefone to call Jill, but no one answered. The automatick answering machine clicked on, and Andrea began to leave a message.

"I was doing my phonicks homework when this show came on!" she exclaimed. "There's a bird on TV that looks just like the one in the photagraph you have. Turn on channel eight, if you're home."

1. _____ 2. _____ 3. _____

4. _____ 5. _____ 6. _____

Writing Activity

Write a paragraph about what you would have done if you were Alexi and became Tsar. Use four words from your spelling list.

_____

_____

_____

_____

_____

_____

_____

_____

_____

_____

_____

© Macmillan/McGraw-Hill

Name_____

Look at the words in each set below. One word in each set is spelled correctly. Use a pencil to fill in the circle next to the correct word. Before you begin, look at the sample set of words. Sample A has been done for you. Do Sample B by yourself. When you are sure you know what to do, you may go on with the rest of the page.

Sample A:

(A) kilometer
(B) killometer
(C) kilommeter
(D) killommeter

Sample B:

(E) phoeton
(F) foton
(G) photton
(H) photon

1. (A) astronat
   (B) astanaut
   (C) astronaut
   (D) astranat

6. (E) telegraph
   (F) tellegraph
   (G) telleggraph
   (H) teleggraph

11. (A) homopphone
    (B) hommophone
    (C) homophone
    (D) hommopphone

16. (E) photoggraphy
    (F) phottography
    (G) photagraphy
    (H) photography

2. (E) autagraph
   (F) autograph
   (G) auttograph
   (H) autograf

7. (A) tellepphone
   (B) telepphone
   (C) tellephone
   (D) telephone

12. (E) phanics
    (F) phonix
    (G) phonnics
    (H) phonics

17. (A) mytth
    (B) mith
    (C) myth
    (D) myeth

3. (A) automattic
   (B) automatic
   (C) auttomatic
   (D) auttomattic

8. (E) tellescope
   (F) telescope
   (G) telesscope
   (H) tellesscope

13. (A) disaster
    (B) dissaster
    (C) disasster
    (D) dissasster

18. (E) machanic
    (F) mechanic
    (G) mecanic
    (H) macanic

4. (E) autommobile
   (F) autommobil
   (G) automobil
   (H) automobile

9. (A) tellevision
   (B) television
   (C) televission
   (D) tellevission

14. (E) astranomer
    (F) astronomer
    (G) astronommer
    (H) asrtonnomer

19. (A) mechanical
    (B) mecanical
    (C) mechanacal
    (D) mecanacal

5. (A) mythical
   (B) mythiccal
   (C) mithical
   (D) mithiccal

10. (E) telegram
    (F) tellegram
    (G) telegramm
    (H) tellegramm

15. (A) photograph
    (B) phottograph
    (C) photoggraph
    (D) phottoggraph

20. (E) telephoto
    (F) tellephoto
    (G) telefoto
    (H) tellefoto

© Macmillan/McGraw-Hill

Name_____

Fold back the paper along the dotted line. Write the words in the blanks as they are read aloud. When you finish the test, unfold the paper. Use the list at the right to correct any spelling mistakes.

1. _____
2. _____
3. _____
4. _____
5. _____
6. _____
7. _____
8. _____
9. _____
10. _____
11. _____
12. _____
13. _____
14. _____
15. _____
16. _____
17. _____
18. _____
19. _____
20. _____

Review Words 21. _____

22. _____

23. _____

Challenge Words 24. _____

25. _____

1. suspect
2. distract
3. export
4. inspect
5. spectator
6. spectacle
7. subtraction
8. tractor
9. import
10. transport
11. transportation
12. attraction
13. inspector
14. missile
15. mission
16. committee
17. intermission
18. portable
19. respect
20. dismiss
21. telescope
22. astronaut
23. photograph
24. spectacular
25. protractor

At Home: Help the student practice the words he or she missed to prepare for the Posttest.

Skunk Scout • Grade 5/Unit 6 **167**

© Macmillan/McGraw-Hill

Name _____

Using the Word Study Steps

1. LOOK at the word.

2. SAY the word aloud.

3. STUDY the letters in the word.

4. WRITE the word.

5. CHECK the word.
Did you spell the word right?
If not, go back to step 1.

Find and Circle

**Find and circle each of the spelling words in this puzzle. Words
may read forward, backward, upward, or downward.**

```
E R E S P E C T S S I M S I D O A A S R
L V T R A N S P O R T I M P O R T T P O
I H S N O I T A T R O P S N A R T T E T
S W M C N E E E T T I M M O C N Z R C C
S N O I S S I M R E T N I T Y F F A T E
I I P D I S T R A C T G N Q M P R C A P
M T P O R T A B L E T C E P S U S T T S
E L C A T C E P S T C E P S N I M I O N
N O I S S I M R J T R A C T O R J O R I
N O I T C A R T B U S E X P O R T N Z O
```

List the words below as you find them in the puzzle.

1. _____   8. _____   15. _____

2. _____   9. _____   16. _____

3. _____   10. _____   17. _____

4. _____   11. _____   18. _____

5. _____   12. _____   19. _____

6. _____   13. _____   20. _____

7. _____   14. _____

© Macmillan/McGraw-Hill

At Home: Review the Word Study Steps above to help the
student spell new words.

Name_____

transport   attraction   intermission   portable
spectacle   committee   dismiss   missile
distract   tractor   export   transportation
respect   import   suspect   inspector
spectator   mission   subtraction   inspect

**Sort each spelling word according to the Latin root it contains.
Then write the words on the lines below.**

mit/miss

1. _____   3. _____   5. _____

2. _____   4. _____

port

1. _____   3. _____   5. _____

2. _____   4. _____

spect

1. _____   3. _____   5. _____

2. _____   4. _____   6. _____

tract

1. _____   3. _____

2. _____   4. _____

© Macmillan/McGraw-Hill

Name_____

transport	attraction	intermission	portable
spectacle	committee	dismiss	missile
distract	tractor	export	transportation
respect	import	suspect	inspector
spectator	mission	subtraction	inspect

Definitions

Write the spelling word that has the same, or almost the same, meaning.

1. group of people assigned to one task _____

2. person who finds out information or judges something _____

3. a task or project _____

4. to send away; a product that is sent from one country to another

   _____

5. able to be moved from one place to another _____

6. special regard for a person or thing _____

7. vehicle used for farming _____

8. the act of removing or taking away _____

9. a person who witnesses an event _____

10. to shift attention away from something _____

Fill in the Blanks

Complete each sentence with a spelling word.

11. I _____ that camping is not much fun in the rain.

12. Cars, buses, trucks, and trains are all forms of _____.

13. Some people like to _____ their food before they eat it.

14. I wonder whether other countries _____ hot dogs from the United States.

15. We left the play during the _____ because we were tired.

© Macmillan/McGraw-Hill

Name _____

Circle the misspelled words in the passage. Write the words correctly on the lines below.

My uncle and I went camping for three days. Our car broke down on the first day, so we lost our means of transportasion. My uncle could only inspekt our car—he couldn't fix it. We found an abandoned tracktor on the second day, but that didn't work, either. Luckily, I had brought my portabel radio with me, so we called for help on the third day. The town put together a comittee and went on a mision to save us.

1. _____ 2. _____ 3. _____

4. _____ 5. _____ 6. _____

Writing Activity

Write a paragraph about why you would or would not like to go camping. Use four words from your spelling list.

_____

_____

_____

_____

_____

_____

_____

_____

_____

_____

_____

_____

© Macmillan/McGraw-Hill

Name_____

Look at the words in each set below. One word in each set is spelled correctly. Use a pencil to fill in the circle next to the correct word. Before you begin, look at the sample set of words. Sample A has been done for you. Do Sample B by yourself. When you are sure you know what to do, you may go on with the rest of the page.

Sample A:

Ⓐ miccroscope
Ⓑ mycroscope
Ⓒ microscope
Ⓓ mykroscope

Sample B:

Ⓔ eequal
Ⓕ equal
Ⓖ equel
Ⓗ equall

1. Ⓐ susspect
   Ⓑ sussppect
   Ⓒ susspect
   Ⓓ suspect

6. Ⓔ specktacle
   Ⓕ spectacle
   Ⓖ specttacle
   Ⓗ spectackle

11. Ⓐ transportashion
    Ⓑ transsportation
    Ⓒ transportation
    Ⓓ transporttation

16. Ⓔ committee
    Ⓕ comittee
    Ⓖ commitee
    Ⓗ comitee

2. Ⓔ distract
   Ⓕ disstract
   Ⓖ disttract
   Ⓗ dissttract

7. Ⓐ subbttraction
   Ⓑ subttraction
   Ⓒ subbtraction
   Ⓓ subtraction

12. Ⓔ attraction
    Ⓕ atraction
    Ⓖ attracktion
    Ⓗ attracshion

17. Ⓐ intermishion
    Ⓑ intermisshion
    Ⓒ intermision
    Ⓓ intermission

3. Ⓐ export
   Ⓑ exxport
   Ⓒ expport
   Ⓓ exporrt

8. Ⓔ tractor
   Ⓕ tracter
   Ⓖ tracktor
   Ⓗ trackter

13. Ⓐ innspecter
    Ⓑ inspecter
    Ⓒ innspector
    Ⓓ inspector

18. Ⓔ porteble
    Ⓕ portable
    Ⓖ portabel
    Ⓗ portebel

4. Ⓔ insspect
   Ⓕ innspect
   Ⓖ inspect
   Ⓗ innsspect

9. Ⓐ impport
   Ⓑ immport
   Ⓒ import
   Ⓓ importt

14. Ⓔ missille
    Ⓕ misile
    Ⓖ missile
    Ⓗ misille

19. Ⓐ respeckt
    Ⓑ resspect
    Ⓒ respect
    Ⓓ rispect

5. Ⓐ spectater
   Ⓑ spectator
   Ⓒ specktator
   Ⓓ specktater

10. Ⓔ transsport
    Ⓕ transport
    Ⓖ transpport
    Ⓗ transsportt

15. Ⓐ mishion
    Ⓑ mision
    Ⓒ mission
    Ⓓ misshion

20. Ⓔ dismiss
    Ⓕ dissmiss
    Ⓖ dissmis
    Ⓗ dismis

© Macmillan/McGraw-Hill

Name _____

Fold back the paper along the dotted line. Write the words in the blanks as they are read aloud. When you finish the test, unfold the paper. Use the list at the right to correct any spelling mistakes.

1. _____
2. _____
3. _____
4. _____
5. _____
6. _____
7. _____
8. _____
9. _____
10. _____
11. _____
12. _____
13. _____
14. _____
15. _____
16. _____
17. _____
18. _____
19. _____
20. _____

Review Words 21. _____
22. _____
23. _____

Challenge Words 24. _____
25. _____

1. cereal
2. terrace
3. gracious
4. echo
5. gigantic
6. ocean
7. atlas
8. clothes
9. territory
10. parasol
11. mortal
12. fury
13. furious
14. January
15. Olympics
16. salute
17. cycle
18. cyclone
19. lunar
20. fortune
21. suspect
22. inspect
23. mission
24. jovial
25. venerable

© Macmillan/McGraw-Hill

At Home: Help the student practice the words he or she missed to prepare for the Posttest.

Name_____

Using the Word Study Steps

1. LOOK at the word.

2. SAY the word aloud.

3. STUDY the letters in the word.

4. WRITE the word.

5. CHECK the word.
   Did you spell the word right?
   If not, go back to step 1.

Fill-Ins

Fill in the missing letters of each word to form a spelling word.

1. c ____ re ____ l

2. te ____ ra ____ e

3. gr ____ ____ ious

4. e ____ ____ o

5. gi ____ an ____ ic

6. o ____ e ____ n

7. at ____ ____ s

8. cl ____ t ____ es

9. ter ____ i ____ ory

10. p ____ ra ____ ol

11. mo ____ ____ al

12. f ____ ____ y

13. f ____ ____ ious

14. J ____ n ____ ____ ry

15. O ____ ____ mp ____ cs

16. s ____ lu ____ e

17. c ____ ____ le

18. cy ____ lo ____ e

19. l ____ n ____ r

20. for ____ ____ ____ e

Use the spelling words above to help you write a poem of at least four lines.

1. _____

2. _____

3. _____

4. _____

At Home: Review the Word Study Steps above to help the student spell new words.

© Macmillan/McGraw-Hill

Name _____

territory	cycle	salute	furious
atlas	lunar	gigantic	echo
gracious	Olympics	fortune	ocean
terrace	parasol	mortal	cyclone
clothes	cereal	January	fury

Sort each spelling word according to the number of syllables it contains. Then write the words on the lines below.

One syllable

1. _____

Two syllables

1. _____
2. _____
3. _____
4. _____
5. _____
6. _____

7. _____
8. _____
9. _____
10. _____
11. _____
12. _____

Three syllables

1. _____
2. _____
3. _____

4. _____
5. _____

Four syllables

1. _____

2. _____

© Macmillan/McGraw-Hill

Name_____

territory	cycle	salute	furious
atlas	lunar	gigantic	echo
gracious	Olympics	fortune	ocean
terrace	parasol	mortal	cyclone
clothes	cereal	January	fury

Complete each sentence below with a spelling word.

1. Hannah helped raise money to build a _____ playground.

2. Whether you win or lose, it's important to be _____.

3. One famous athlete has his picture on a box of _____.

4. The _____ are held every four years in a different country.

5. You can look in an _____ to find a map of where the Olympics will be held.

6. The new playground will not cost a _____ to build.

7. You can hear the _____ of your own voice if the Olympic stadium is empty.

8. Many athletes train by swimming in the _____ during the warmer months.

9. Putting on _____ can sometimes be challenging for people with disabilities.

10. The new school gym program will begin in _____.

Write On!

Use each spelling word in a sentence.

11. parasol _____

12. cyclone _____

13. terrace _____

14. mortal _____

15. territory _____

© Macmillan/McGraw-Hill

Name

Circle the misspelled words in the passage. Write the words correctly on the lines below.

Jake heard his footsteps ecko as he walked into the jigantic stadium. Today he would compete in his first Olimpics. He had been training since Janyuary. He swam in the osean three times a week and had been watching his diet closely. This morning he had eaten a bowl of sereal and and a piece of toast. The day he had been waiting for had finally come.

1. _____   2. _____   3. _____

4. _____   5. _____   6. _____

Writing Activity

Write a paragraph about a time when you helped someone accomplish a goal. Use four words from your spelling list.

_____

_____

_____

_____

_____

_____

_____

_____

_____

_____

_____

_____

_____

© Macmillan/McGraw-Hill

Name_____

Look at the words in each set below. One word in each set is spelled correctly. Use a pencil to fill in the circle next to the correct word. Before you begin, look at the sample set of words. Sample A has been done for you. Do Sample B by yourself. When you are sure you know what to do, you may go on with the rest of the page.

Sample A:

Ⓐ Wednesday
Ⓑ Wendsday
Ⓒ Whendsday
Ⓓ Wensday

Sample B:

Ⓔ Satturday
Ⓕ Saturday
Ⓖ Satterday
Ⓗ Saterday

1. Ⓐ cerreal
   Ⓑ sereal
   Ⓒ cereal
   Ⓓ cerial

2. Ⓔ terrase
   Ⓕ terace
   Ⓖ terrace
   Ⓗ terase

3. Ⓐ gracious
   Ⓑ grashious
   Ⓒ graceious
   Ⓓ grayshus

4. Ⓔ echoe
   Ⓕ ecko
   Ⓖ ecco
   Ⓗ echo

5. Ⓐ giggantic
   Ⓑ gigantic
   Ⓒ jigantic
   Ⓓ jiggantic

6. Ⓔ ocean
   Ⓕ ohcean
   Ⓖ oshun
   Ⓗ oacean

7. Ⓐ attlas
   Ⓑ atlass
   Ⓒ atlas
   Ⓓ attlass

8. Ⓔ cloathez
   Ⓕ clothez
   Ⓖ cloathes
   Ⓗ clothes

9. Ⓐ territorry
   Ⓑ territory
   Ⓒ teritory
   Ⓓ teritorry

10. Ⓔ parasol
    Ⓕ parassol
    Ⓖ parrasol
    Ⓗ parasoll

11. Ⓐ moretal
    Ⓑ mortle
    Ⓒ mortel
    Ⓓ mortal

12. Ⓔ fuery
    Ⓕ fury
    Ⓖ fuiry
    Ⓗ furey

13. Ⓐ fuirious
    Ⓑ fureious
    Ⓒ furious
    Ⓓ fuerious

14. Ⓔ January
    Ⓕ Jannuary
    Ⓖ Januery
    Ⓗ Januarry

15. Ⓐ Olympicks
    Ⓑ Olimpics
    Ⓒ Ollympics
    Ⓓ Olympics

16. Ⓔ selute
    Ⓕ salute
    Ⓖ sallute
    Ⓗ sellute

17. Ⓐ cicle
    Ⓑ scycle
    Ⓒ cycle
    Ⓓ scicle

18. Ⓔ cyclone
    Ⓕ ciclone
    Ⓖ scyclone
    Ⓗ sciclone

19. Ⓐ loonar
    Ⓑ luner
    Ⓒ lunear
    Ⓓ lunar

20. Ⓔ foretune
    Ⓕ fortune
    Ⓖ fourtune
    Ⓗ fortun

© Macmillan/McGraw-Hill

Name_____

Fold back the paper along the dotted line. Write the words in the blanks as they are read aloud. When you finish the test, unfold the paper. Use the list at the right to correct any spelling mistakes.

1. _____
2. _____
3. _____
4. _____
5. _____
6. _____
7. _____
8. _____
9. _____
10. _____
11. _____
12. _____
13. _____
14. _____
15. _____
16. _____
17. _____
18. _____
19. _____
20. _____

Review Words 21. _____

22. _____

23. _____

Challenge Words 24. _____

25. _____

1. uniform
2. bisect
3. tricycle
4. triplet
5. triple
6. unicorn
7. unify
8. unison
9. universe
10. unicycle
11. biweekly
12. binoculars
13. triangle
14. bicycle
15. trio
16. century
17. centipede
18. centimeter
19. tripod
20. university
21. cereal
22. terrace
23. atlas
24. bilingual
25. trilogy

© Macmillan/McGraw-Hill

At Home: Help the student practice the words he or she missed to prepare for the Posttest.

Name_____

Using the Word Study Steps

1. LOOK at the word.

2. SAY the word aloud.

3. STUDY the letters in the word.

4. WRITE the word.

5. CHECK the word.
Did you spell the word right?
If not, go back to step 1.

Find and Circle

Find and circle each of the spelling words in this puzzle. Words may read forward, backward, upward, downward, or diagonally.

```
E  N  B  B  E  S  N  N  K  N  C  J  K  O  T  J  T
U  D  P  I  I  R  R  A  R  I  O  T  G  R  I  R  E
N  E  E  U  S  W  Q  A  R  O  E  S  I  S  I  T  S
I  L  L  P  N  E  E  T  L  X  C  P  I  C  Y  R  R
F  P  L  O  I  I  C  E  F  U  L  I  Y  N  G  I  E
O  I  I  Z  Y  T  V  T  K  E  C  C  N  E  U  A  V
R  R  F  M  K  I  N  E  T  L  L  O  N  U  T  N  I
M  T  Y  F  I  N  U  E  R  E  Y  N  N  R  Q  G  N
E  L  C  Y  C  I  N  U  C  S  U  T  I  I  B  L  U
R  E  T  E  M  I  T  N  E  C  I  P  R  L  B  E  G
E  L  C  Y  C  I  B  A  L  K  O  T  I  I  C  M  R
C  E  N  T  U  R  Y  Q  B  D  D  D  Y  B  O  O  Q
```

List the words below as you find them in the puzzle.

1. _____   8. _____   15. _____

2. _____   9. _____   16. _____

3. _____   10. _____   17. _____

4. _____   11. _____   18. _____

5. _____   12. _____   19. _____

6. _____   13. _____   20. _____

7. _____   14. _____

At Home: Review the Word Study Steps above to help the student spell new words.

© Macmillan/McGraw-Hill

Name_____

uniform	unison	bisect	tricycle
trio	tripod	university	unify
universe	biweekly	triangle	bicycle
binoculars	unicycle	centipede	unicorn
triplet	centimeter	triple	century

Sort each spelling word according to its prefix. Then write the words on the lines below.

uni-

1. _____

2. _____

3. _____

4. _____

5. _____

6. _____

7. _____

bi-

1. _____

2. _____

3. _____

4. _____

tri-

1. _____

2. _____

3. _____

4. _____

5. _____

6. _____

cent-

1. _____

2. _____

3. _____

© Macmillan/McGraw-Hill

Name_____

uniform	unison	bisect	tricycle
trio	tripod	university	unify
universe	biweekly	triangle	bicycle
binoculars	unicycle	centipede	unicorn
triplet	centimeter	triple	century

Definitions

Write the spelling word that has the same, or almost the same, meaning.

1. a name for three musical performers _____

2. a wormlike animal with many pairs of legs _____

3. an imaginary horselike animal with a single, long horn _____

4. a figure with three sides and three angles _____

5. occurring every two weeks _____

6. a group or set of three, usually in music _____

7. a mode of transportation that has one wheel _____

8. to cut into two equal parts _____

9. a unit of length _____

10. together or at the same time _____

Fill in the Blanks

Complete each sentence with a spelling word.

11. Each member of the balloonist club wore a red _____.

12. It would be strange to see a grownup riding a _____.

13. Ballooning can bring people closer together and _____ an entire state.

14. One man improved the hot-air balloon about a _____ ago.

15. Ballooning can make you feel like you are exploring the _____.

16. Using _____, you can see people below from hundreds of feet in the air.

© Macmillan/McGraw-Hill

Name_____

Circle the misspelled words in the passage. Write the words correctly on the lines below.

      Jean-Pierre Blanchard and John Jefferies took one of the most daring trips of the sentury. They practiced biweeklie to make sure that everything went smoothly. The trip was going well until the temperature got colder, and they began to sink. "Help us!" they cried in unisun. To make the balloon lighter, Blanchard removed part of his unaform. Using his banoculars, Jefferies could see a small place to land. On the way down, they missed a tree branch by less than a centumeter.

1. _____ 2. _____ 3. _____

4. _____ 5. _____ 6. _____

Writing Activity

Write a paragraph about where you would go if you had a chance to ride in a hot-air balloon. Use four words from your spelling list.

_____

_____

_____

_____

_____

_____

_____

_____

_____

_____

_____

© Macmillan/McGraw-Hill

Name_____

Look at the words in each set below. One word in each set is spelled correctly. Use a pencil to fill in the circle next to the correct word. Before you begin, look at the sample set of words. Sample A has been done for you. Do Sample B by yourself. When you are sure you know what to do, you may go on with the rest of the page.

Sample A:

- Ⓐ byplane
- Ⓑ biplane
- Ⓒ bipplane
- Ⓓ biplain

Sample B:

- Ⓔ triddent
- Ⓕ triedent
- Ⓖ trident
- Ⓗ trydent

1.
- Ⓐ unnifform
- Ⓑ unniform
- Ⓒ unifform
- Ⓓ uniform

6.
- Ⓔ uniccorn
- Ⓕ unicorn
- Ⓖ unnicorn
- Ⓗ unicorrn

11.
- Ⓐ biweekly
- Ⓑ byweekly
- Ⓒ bieweekly
- Ⓓ biweakly

16.
- Ⓔ centurry
- Ⓕ centtury
- Ⓖ century
- Ⓗ centturry

2.
- Ⓔ biesect
- Ⓕ bissect
- Ⓖ bisect
- Ⓗ bysect

7.
- Ⓐ unify
- Ⓑ unnify
- Ⓒ unefy
- Ⓓ uniffy

12.
- Ⓔ bynoculars
- Ⓕ binnoculars
- Ⓖ binoculars
- Ⓗ binocculars

17.
- Ⓐ centipede
- Ⓑ centtipede
- Ⓒ centipeed
- Ⓓ centippede

3.
- Ⓐ trycycle
- Ⓑ triscyckle
- Ⓒ tricycle
- Ⓓ tricicle

8.
- Ⓔ unisson
- Ⓕ unnison
- Ⓖ unison
- Ⓗ unnisson

13.
- Ⓐ tryangle
- Ⓑ triangel
- Ⓒ triangle
- Ⓓ trieangle

18.
- Ⓔ centimetter
- Ⓕ centimmeter
- Ⓖ centimeter
- Ⓗ centimmetter

4.
- Ⓔ triplet
- Ⓕ tripplet
- Ⓖ tripllet
- Ⓗ trippllett

9.
- Ⓐ univearse
- Ⓑ unniverse
- Ⓒ univverse
- Ⓓ universe

14.
- Ⓔ bisickle
- Ⓕ biecycle
- Ⓖ bycycle
- Ⓗ bicycle

19.
- Ⓐ tripod
- Ⓑ triepod
- Ⓒ trypod
- Ⓓ trippod

5.
- Ⓐ tripel
- Ⓑ tripple
- Ⓒ triple
- Ⓓ trippel

10.
- Ⓔ unicycle
- Ⓕ unicicle
- Ⓖ uniscycle
- Ⓗ unnicycle

15.
- Ⓐ trio
- Ⓑ treeo
- Ⓒ trieo
- Ⓓ tryo

20.
- Ⓔ universsity
- Ⓕ universeity
- Ⓖ univversity
- Ⓗ university

© Macmillan/McGraw-Hill

Name_____

Fold back the paper along the dotted line. Write the words in the blanks as they are read aloud. When you finish the test, unfold the paper. Use the list at the right to correct any spelling mistakes.

1. _____
2. _____
3. _____
4. _____
5. _____
6. _____
7. _____
8. _____
9. _____
10. _____
11. _____
12. _____
13. _____
14. _____
15. _____
16. _____
17. _____
18. _____
19. _____
20. _____

Review Words 21. _____
22. _____
23. _____

Challenge Words 24. _____
25. _____

1. collapsible
2. breakable
3. affordable
4. usable
5. bearable
6. favorable
7. capable
8. enjoyable
9. honorable
10. convertible
11. invisible
12. reasonable
13. respectable
14. sensible
15. unbelievable
16. possible
17. suitable
18. laughable
19. likable
20. comfortable
21. uniform
22. bicycle
23. triangle
24. manageable
25. tangible

© Macmillan/McGraw-Hill

At Home: Help the student practice the words he or she missed to prepare for the Posttest.

Name_____

Using the Word Study Steps

1. LOOK at the word.

2. SAY the word aloud.

3. STUDY the letters in the word.

4. WRITE the word.

5. CHECK the word.
   Did you spell the word right?
   If not, go back to step 1.

Fill-Ins

Fill in the missing letters of each word to form a spelling word.

1. collaps ___ ___ ___ e

2. break ___ ___ ___ e

3. afford ___ ___ ___ e

4. us ___ ___ ___ e

5. bear ___ ___ ___ e

6. favor ___ ___ ___ e

7. cap ___ ___ l ___

8. enjoy ___ ___ ___ ___

9. honor ___ ___ ___ e

10. convert ___ ___ ___ e

11. invis ___ ___ l ___

12. reason ___ ___ l ___

13. respect ___ ___ ___ e

14. sens ___ ___ l ___

15. unbeliev ___ ___ ___ e

16. poss ___ ___ l ___

17. suit ___ ___ ___ e

18. laugh ___ ___ ___ ___

19. lik ___ ___ ___ ___

20. comfort ___ ___ ___ ___

Alphabetical Order

Use the lines below to write the spelling words in alphabetical order.

1. _____
2. _____
3. _____
4. _____
5. _____

6. _____
7. _____
8. _____
9. _____
10. _____

11. _____
12. _____
13. _____
14. _____
15. _____

16. _____
17. _____
18. _____
19. _____
20. _____

© Macmillan/McGraw-Hill

At Home: Review the Word Study Steps above to help the student spell new words.

Name_____

honorable	favorable	invisible	likable
enjoyable	collapsible	laughable	suitable
breakable	unbelievable	sensible	possible
convertible	affordable	respectable	comfortable
usable	bearable	reasonable	capable

Sort each spelling word according to its ending. Then write the words on the lines below.

-able

1. _____
2. _____
3. _____
4. _____
5. _____

6. _____
7. _____
8. _____
9. _____
10. _____

11. _____
12. _____
13. _____
14. _____
15. _____

-ible

1. _____
2. _____
3. _____

4. _____
5. _____

Make a Puzzle

Make up a puzzle of your own using the space on this page. Give it to someone else to solve. Be sure to include at least five spelling words in your puzzle.

© Macmillan/McGraw-Hill

honorable	usable	affordable	sensible	suitable
enjoyable	favorable	bearable	respectable	possible
breakable	collapsible	invisible	reasonable	comfortable
convertible	unbelievable	laughable	likable	capable

Sentence Completions

Complete each sentence below with a spelling word.

1. Many tiny creatures are _____ to the human eye without a microscope.

2. Dennis likes microscopes and thinks that looking through them is _____.

3. The scientists had a _____ tent that could fold up quickly.

4. Those delicate glass test tubes are _____, so be careful with them.

5. Dennis is a _____ scientist who can easily do many things.

6. That broken microscope is not _____ and needs to be fixed.

7. She is a _____ scientist because her work is always well researched.

8. Being a scientist is an _____ job because it helps future generations.

9. Some colleges are expensive, but others are more _____.

10. We had never seen so much ash before—it was _____!

Similar Meanings

Write the spelling word that has the same, or almost the same, meaning.

11. cozy _____

12. pleasant _____

13. capable of being dealt with _____

14. practical _____

15. having good sense _____

16. capable of happening _____

17. funny _____

18. proper _____

© Macmillan/McGraw-Hill

Name_____

Circle the misspelled words in the passage. Write the words correctly on the lines provided.

   Welcome to the Hawaii Science College! We do our best to make getting a science degree affordible for everyone. You will find the cost of our classes reasonble. Also, we want your time here as a student to be enjoyabl. Our teachers are likeble people who will help you meet the challenge of college-level homework. With a degree from our school, anything is possable! So let's start the tour. Please let me know whether we can do anything to make your visit here more comfortible.

1. _____   2. _____   3. _____

4. _____   5. _____   6. _____

Writing Activity

Write a paragraph about your favorite outdoor activity or school subject. Use four words from your spelling list.

_____
_____
_____
_____
_____
_____
_____
_____
_____
_____
_____
_____

© Macmillan/McGraw-Hill

Name_____

Look at the words in each set below. One word in each set is spelled correctly. Use a pencil to fill in the circle next to the correct word. Before you begin, look at the sample set of words. Sample A has been done for you. Do Sample B by yourself. When you are sure you know what to do, you may go on with the rest of the page.

Sample A:
- Ⓐ invinceable
- Ⓑ invincable
- Ⓒ invincible
- Ⓓ invinceible

Sample B:
- Ⓔ dooible
- Ⓕ doible
- Ⓖ doable
- Ⓗ dooable

1.
- Ⓐ collapseable
- Ⓑ collapseible
- Ⓒ collapsible
- Ⓓ collapsable

6.
- Ⓔ favoreable
- Ⓕ favorible
- Ⓖ favorable
- Ⓗ favoreible

11.
- Ⓐ invisible
- Ⓑ invisable
- Ⓒ invissible
- Ⓓ inivissable

16.
- Ⓔ possible
- Ⓕ possable
- Ⓖ posible
- Ⓗ posable

2.
- Ⓔ breakable
- Ⓕ breakible
- Ⓖ brakeable
- Ⓗ brakeible

7.
- Ⓐ capeible
- Ⓑ capeable
- Ⓒ capable
- Ⓓ capible

12.
- Ⓔ reasonnable
- Ⓕ reasonible
- Ⓖ reasonable
- Ⓗ reasonnible

17.
- Ⓐ suitible
- Ⓑ suitable
- Ⓒ suiteable
- Ⓓ suiteible

3.
- Ⓐ affordable
- Ⓑ afordable
- Ⓒ affordible
- Ⓓ afordible

8.
- Ⓔ enjoyyible
- Ⓕ enjoyyable
- Ⓖ enjoyible
- Ⓗ enjoyable

13.
- Ⓐ respectible
- Ⓑ respectable
- Ⓒ respecttible
- Ⓓ respecttable

18.
- Ⓔ laghable
- Ⓕ laghible
- Ⓖ laughible
- Ⓗ laughable

4.
- Ⓔ usabel
- Ⓕ useible
- Ⓖ usible
- Ⓗ usable

9.
- Ⓐ honorible
- Ⓑ honorable
- Ⓒ honorrable
- Ⓓ honorrible

14.
- Ⓔ senseable
- Ⓕ sensable
- Ⓖ senseible
- Ⓗ sensible

19.
- Ⓐ likeible
- Ⓑ likable
- Ⓒ likible
- Ⓓ likkable

5.
- Ⓐ bearible
- Ⓑ bearable
- Ⓒ bearrable
- Ⓓ bearrible

10.
- Ⓔ convertible
- Ⓕ convertable
- Ⓖ converttible
- Ⓗ converttable

15.
- Ⓐ unbelievible
- Ⓑ unbelieveible
- Ⓒ unbelieveable
- Ⓓ unbelievable

20.
- Ⓔ comforttable
- Ⓕ comforttible
- Ⓖ comfortible
- Ⓗ comfortable

© Macmillan/McGraw-Hill

Name _____

Read each sentence. If an underlined word is spelled wrong, fill in the circle that goes with that word. If no word is spelled wrong, fill in the circle below NONE. Read Sample A and do Sample B.

NONE

A. I <u>suspect</u> that there was a <u>disaster</u> during <u>intermishun</u>.　A. Ⓐ Ⓑ ⬤ Ⓓ
　　　A　　　　　　　　　　B　　　　　　　C

NONE

B. I saw the <u>spectacle</u> at the <u>Olimpics</u> with <u>binoculars</u>.　B. Ⓔ Ⓕ Ⓖ Ⓗ
　　　　　　E　　　　　　F　　　　　　G

NONE

1. My <u>automobile</u> and <u>television</u> make me <u>comfertible</u>.　1. Ⓐ Ⓑ Ⓒ Ⓓ
　　　　A　　　　　　B　　　　　　　C

NONE

2. The <u>myth</u> involved a <u>unacorn</u> and an <u>invisible</u> forest.　2. Ⓔ Ⓕ Ⓖ Ⓗ
　　　E　　　　　　F　　　　　　G

NONE

3. Being an <u>astronaut</u> is a <u>respectable</u> and <u>enjoyibel</u> job.　3. Ⓐ Ⓑ Ⓒ Ⓓ
　　　　　A　　　　　　B　　　　　C

NONE

4. They took a <u>fotograph</u> of the <u>gigantic</u> <u>ocean</u>.　4. Ⓔ Ⓕ Ⓖ Ⓗ
　　　　　　E　　　　　F　　　G

NONE

5. The <u>automobile</u> and <u>bicicle</u> are forms of <u>transportation</u>.　5. Ⓐ Ⓑ Ⓒ Ⓓ
　　　　A　　　　　B　　　　　　C

NONE

6. I'll be <u>furius</u> if you <u>distract</u> me while I'm on the <u>telephone</u>!　6. Ⓔ Ⓕ Ⓖ Ⓗ
　　　　E　　　　F　　　　　　　　G

NONE

7. The <u>comitee</u> wanted to <u>inspect</u> the school <u>uniform</u>.　7. Ⓐ Ⓑ Ⓒ Ⓓ
　　　A　　　　　B　　　　　　C

NONE

8. It's <u>possible</u> to have a <u>rispectible</u> job and earn a <u>fortune</u>.　8. Ⓔ Ⓕ Ⓖ Ⓗ
　　　E　　　　　F　　　　　　　G

NONE

9. It's not always <u>enjoyable</u> to ride a <u>bicycle</u> in <u>Janaruy</u>.　9. Ⓐ Ⓑ Ⓒ Ⓓ
　　　　　　A　　　　　B　　　C

NONE

10. Is the story about the <u>unicorn</u> a <u>mith</u>, or is it <u>possible</u>?　10. Ⓔ Ⓕ Ⓖ Ⓗ
　　　　　　　E　　F　　　　G

NONE

11. <u>Comfortable</u> <u>transpertaton</u> is a product of this <u>century</u>.　11. Ⓐ Ⓑ Ⓒ Ⓓ
　　　A　　　　B　　　　　　　　C

NONE

12. I'd like to <u>inpsect</u> that <u>gigantic</u> <u>territory</u> near the lake.　12. Ⓔ Ⓕ Ⓖ Ⓗ
　　　　　E　　　　F　　　G

© Macmillan/McGraw-Hill

Name_____

13. We saw a <u>photograph</u> of an <u>astronaut</u> on <u>telivison</u>.
              A   B   C

NONE
13. Ⓐ Ⓑ Ⓒ Ⓓ

14. I was <u>furious</u> when the <u>spectator</u> tried to <u>destract</u> me!
           E   F   G

NONE
14. Ⓔ Ⓕ Ⓖ Ⓗ

15. The <u>mechanic</u> had a <u>jigantic</u> tool shaped like a <u>triangle</u>.
          A   B   C

NONE
15. Ⓐ Ⓑ Ⓒ Ⓓ

16. The ring brought <u>respect</u> and good <u>fortune</u> for
                    E   F

a <u>sentury</u>.
  G

NONE
16. Ⓔ Ⓕ Ⓖ Ⓗ

17. The ring made it <u>possable</u> to be <u>invisible</u> to a <u>spectator</u>.
                 A   B   C

NONE
17. Ⓐ Ⓑ Ⓒ Ⓓ

18. They formed a <u>committee</u> to find a <u>portable</u> <u>telefone</u>.
                E   F   G

NONE
18. Ⓔ Ⓕ Ⓖ Ⓗ

19. An <u>autamibile</u> is a quicker form of <u>transportation</u>
       A   B

than a <u>unicorn</u>.
     C

NONE
19. Ⓐ Ⓑ Ⓒ Ⓓ

20. <u>January</u> is a nice time to <u>photograph</u> the <u>oshun</u>.
    E   F   G

NONE
20. Ⓔ Ⓕ Ⓖ Ⓗ

21. The <u>mechanic</u> wore a <u>unaform</u> and earned <u>respect</u>.
      A   B   C

NONE
21. Ⓐ Ⓑ Ⓒ Ⓓ

22. The pocket of the <u>comfortable</u> <u>uniform</u> had a red <u>tryangle</u>.
                E   F   G

NONE
22. Ⓔ Ⓕ Ⓖ Ⓗ

23. The tsar wore <u>comfortable</u> <u>clothes</u> but commanded
             A   B

<u>rispect</u>.
  C

NONE
23. Ⓐ Ⓑ Ⓒ Ⓓ

24. To the <u>astronaut</u>, the whole <u>territory</u> seemed <u>invisabel</u>.
        E   F   G

NONE
24. Ⓔ Ⓕ Ⓖ Ⓗ

25. He spent his <u>forchun</u> on new <u>clothes</u> and an <u>automobile</u>.
         A   B   C

NONE
25. Ⓐ Ⓑ Ⓒ Ⓓ

© Macmillan/McGraw-Hill